Longman exam practice kit

A-Level Biology

Alan Cornwell

Ruth Miller

Series Editors
Geoff Black and Stuart Wall

Titles available

A-Level
Biology
Business Studies
Chemistry
Mathematics
Psychology
Sociology

Addison Wesley Longman Ltd,
Edinburgh Gate, Harlow,
Essex CM20 2JE, England
and Associated Companies throughout the World.

First Published 1997

ISBN 0582-30386-9

British Library Cataloguing-in-Publication Data
A catalogue record for this book is available from the British Library.

Printed in Great Britain by Henry Ling Ltd, at the Dorset Press
Dorchester Dorset

Contents

Acknowledgements

We are grateful to the following examination groups for permission to reproduce questions from past examination papers:

The Associated Examining Board
EDEXCEL Foundation
Northern Examinations and Assessment Board
Oxford & Cambridge Examinations & Assessment Council
Welsh Joint Education Committee

The above examination groups are not responsible for the accuracy or method of working in the answers given.

Whilst every effort has been made to trace the owners of copyright material we take this opportunity to offer our apologies to any copyright holders whose rights we may have unwittingly infringed.

part I

Preparing for the examination

Preparing for the examination

KNOW YOUR SYLLABUS

It is very important to get to know your syllabus before you are too far into your course. Although all Biology syllabuses will have a common core of biological knowledge, there are variations, both in the content and in the way in which it is examined, which you should be aware of from the beginning. It is unlikely that you will have been able to choose which syllabus you follow, unless you are working on your own, but your teachers will have considered which one they feel is best.
Find out whether your course is:

- **Modular** The syllabus is divided into units, or modules, which are examined separately and papers can be taken throughout the course.
- **Linear** The syllabus may be divided into units, which are examined on different papers, but all the papers are taken during one examination period.

If your course is modular, you will need to know:

- how many modules you need to study;
- whether there are compulsory and optional modules;
- in which order you are going to study the different modules;
- when you will be entered for the examinations.

For all syllabuses, there is a coursework requirement, so you need to establish how much you are expected to submit and when the deadlines are. All the exam boards publish a timetable of examination dates well in advance, so it should not be difficult to find out when you will be expected to sit papers. The different boards do have examinations at different times of the year: UCLES has examinations for their modular papers in November, March and June, whereas London(EdExcel) papers are sat in January and June.

PLANNING YOUR REVISION

Having established which papers you are sitting and when the examinations are, put the dates in your diary – you need to plan your revision well ahead! With the present syllabuses, whether modular or linear, you will have a pretty good idea of the topics that are likely to be examined on each paper. You will not normally be expected to know the entire syllabus for each separate paper. This does lead to a temptation to leave revision until the last moment, which is most unwise. Throughout your period of working towards an examination, you should check your understanding of the topics as you progress. Many students find that it is helpful to rewrite notes taken in lessons, adding background material from their textbooks, so that they have a complete record of a topic. Even if this is not the best way for you, you should read through your notes as soon as possible after a lesson to make sure you understand them. If there are points which you do not understand, check with your textbooks or try to see your teacher before the next lesson. Often the teacher will be only too pleased to go over a topic again to make sure that the class has understood. In this way you will have a firm base for understanding future work and you will have taken the first steps in the learning process.

The next step is to revise regularly. If you do not look at previously understood material for several months, you are likely to forget the details and eventually much of your understanding. Repetition is an important tool in reinforcing your understanding, so build revision time into your weekly work plan. It is sensible to do this, especially if your examinations are to be spread throughout your course. It is not wise to attempt to commit everything to memory in a short time. Many of the questions set on examination papers require you to be able to use your knowledge to interpret unfamiliar data and you are not likely to be able to do this if you do not have a good, sound understanding of the syllabus material gained from consistent review of each topic.

In addition to planning your revision time, plan some relaxation time as well. You are unlikely to be able to work flat out for more than three quarters of an hour to an hour at a time, so it is probably more sensible to plan two shorter revision periods rather than one long one.

How should you revise? There is no one answer to this question, as everyone finds different methods to suit themselves. As we have mentioned, some students find it helpful to write up their **class notes**. Many people find the use of **keywords**, **diagrams** and **flow charts** helpful. If you build up a set of cards on to which you put the main facts, these can be kept in a file and are handy reminders of the basic details. These are especially valuable if you build them up for yourself, rather than copying the information from textbooks or buying sets of cards. There is no substitute for your own notes, as you have probably discovered if you have tried to work from notes taken by a friend.

Active revision is better than passive revision. Passive revision simply involves reading through notes and is probably the wisest strategy the night before the examination, when you are just reminding yourself of the topics. Active revision reinforces the learning process and involves you doing something different with the topics. The use of past examination questions, writing plans for essays, making lists of key points – all these will help fix the information in your memory. Reading around your subject is also of value. Articles in *New Scientist* or *Biological Sciences Review* may help to fill in some details for you, apart from increasing your general knowledge of the subject.

When you use examination questions as part of your revision, first of all revise the relevant topic, then attempt the answer without referring to your notes. When you have completed the question, check with your notes to see if you have included all the relevant details. If you use the questions in this book, remember that the answers given are not always model answers. In many cases we have given the obvious answers, but there are often alternatives and different ways of expressing an answer, so these illustrate one way of selecting and organising material. If your answers differ from the ones given, compare the two and decide whether or not your answer is along the right lines.

TYPES OF EXAMINATION QUESTIONS

Broadly speaking, there are two types of examination questions:

- those that test your knowledge and understanding of a topic;
- those that test your skill in using your biological knowledge to analyse and interpret data, often presented in an unfamiliar way.

Most of the papers you sit will involve answering **structured questions**, writing your answers in the spaces provided in the booklet. Remember that the **number of lines** or spaces left on the question paper indicates the

length of answer that is expected. The **mark allocation** at the end of each section of a question is a further indication of the length and detail required.

- **Short structured questions**, such as naming parts on diagrams, filling in gaps in a prose passage, completing tables and tick boxes, are all straightforward ways of testing your knowledge and understanding.
- **Longer structured questions** may involve some data-handling. You may be asked to plot a graph of data supplied, to carry out a calculation or read and interpret a passage. Where you are supplied with data that require interpretation, take time to read through all the parts of the question so that you know exactly what is expected of you. Often in this type of question, you may be asked to design an experiment or comment on an experimental procedure, so be sure that your revision has included all the relevant practical work associated with the topics involved.You may be expected to write essays or longer passages of continuous prose. The London(EdExcel) module tests have a 10-mark free prose question and the synoptic papers have essays. The other boards (including UCLES, AEB, WJEC and NEAB) have questions and sections of questions where you are expected to write in continuous prose. If you are expected to write an essay, the instructions on the paper will often indicate how much time you should allow for the question and also the allocation of marks. In London(EdExcel) synoptic papers, for example, you are recommended to spend at least 35 minutes on the essay and you are told that marks are awarded for the scientific content, the balance and cover of the topic and for the coherence and clarity of your expression. You can afford to spend some time planning what you are going to write about so that your answer is relevant, covers the topic and is written in a good style, avoiding grammatical and spelling errors. You may feel that essay writing is not relevant to modern Biology syllabuses, but one of the skills that you need is an ability to communicate your knowledge in continuous prose as well as in tables, charts and diagrams.

COMMAND WORDS USED IN QUESTIONS

A number of different command words are commonly used in examination questions and it is a good idea to be familiar with these, so that you can deliver the information required in the correct format.

Direct questions Asked in many papers, these include:
– '**What** is the effect of substance A?'
– '**Why** does the muscle contract?'
– '**Where** is the sarcoplasmic reticulum?'
– '**How** are monosaccharides formed from disaccharides?'
With this type of question you know exactly what you have to do and reference to the mark allocation should indicate the depth of your answer.

Give, State, Name These instructions are straightforward commands you will encounter more often and are usually used where short or one-word answers are required.

Define Requires a statement outlining what is meant by a particular term, e.g. 'Define the term osmosis' would encourage you to give a straight definition of the process.

Describe Often used when an account of an experiment is asked for, e.g. 'Describe how you would use the apparatus to measure the rate of uptake of oxygen', or it may be used to get you to observe a graph and describe the difference in the curves. In both cases, you are not being asked to account for, or explain, what is happening.

Comment on This term has often appeared and is slightly different from 'describe': it could be said to mean 'Describe and give some explanation for ...' This is a difficult one to interpret and if you are in any doubt, it would be advisable to check past examination papers, together with the mark schemes, to find out exactly what marks were awarded for. Your teacher may be able to help you, as some boards do publish mark schemes and circulate them to centres. How much information you include in your description depends on the mark allocation given at the end of the sub-section of the question.

Compare This is asking for similarities *and* differences, so remember to give *both.*

Distinguish between Unlike 'compare', requires the *differences* only. Sometimes you may be asked 'Give two similarities between...' or 'State two differences between...', in which case only give TWO. It is not clever to give more than two, leaving the examiner to choose. The first two answers will be marked and the rest ignored, so even if you had two correct answers in your list they would not score marks unless they were the first two you wrote. Apart from any other considerations, it is a waste of time giving more than is required as time in the examination is precious.

Explain Means exactly what it says: you should give a biological explanation. 'Explain the importance of ATP in muscle contraction' would require details of the association of ATP with the formation of cross bridges between actin and myosin.

Calculate Invites you to carry out a calculation. You should always show the steps of your working, even if not asked to do so, as marks are often awarded for method even if you make an arithmetical error. Such questions often involve substituting figures in a given formula. You should be as accurate as possible and beware of rounding figures up or down too soon.

Draw a graph This is another self-explanatory command. You will be provided with the figures and you may need to select a suitable scale for the size of graph paper provided. It is best to draw the graph in pencil, so that any errors can be rectified easily.

Suggest an explanation for You may be asked to do this where you are not expected to know what the correct answer is, or where you have been presented with an unfamiliar situation. Your answer should draw on your biological knowledge of similar situations and in such cases a wide range of answers could be accepted, as long as they are sensible.

Predict the result Similarly, this asks you to use your judgement and biological knowledge to make a sensible suggestion.

Discuss Requires you to describe and evaluate a situation, putting forward more than one opinion. This type of command is often associated with essay topics and your best strategy is to plan such answers before beginning to write.

THE EXAMINATION

Make sure you know:

- the date of your examination
- where your examination is being held
- the time of day; morning or afternoon
- which paper you are sitting

- whether you need to take in any equipment such as a ruler or a calculator
- your examination number.

It is also a good idea to let someone at home know your examination timetable, so that you are not allowed to oversleep!

When you get into the examination room:

- relax as much as you can: if your revision has been thorough then you should not be thrown into a panic when you see the questions
- check that you have been given the correct paper: if there are several different examinations being held in one big room it is easy for the invigilators to make a mistake, especially if there are different optional papers
- read through the instructions on the front cover carefully
- read through the questions carefully, trying to ensure you answer relevantly
- work steadily through the paper, leaving any difficult areas to go back to later
- it is best not to spend a long time puzzling away at one question as you may have to rush others or even omit questions through lack of time
- be aware of the mark allocations
- write legibly and in good English as an examiner cannot give marks for information that cannot be read
- if you finish with some time to spare, go through and check your work
- avoid missing out questions, or parts of questions, as this reduces the total of marks available to you: it is better to write something than to leave a gap
- try to ignore what other people are doing around you: you need to concentrate all the time to make sure you do yourself justice for all the hard work you have put in.

HOW TO USE THIS BOOK

For *each* of the 8 topic areas in Part II, you will find:

- Revision Tips
- Topic Outline

To help make your revision *active* you will also find:

- Revision Activity
- Examination Questions

Answers and grading of these can be found in Part III, together with an *extra question and student answer* on each topic.

Part IV gives you the opportunity to time yourself on some practice questions

part II

Topic areas, summaries and questions

1 Molecules, cells and organelles

REVISION TIPS

A knowledge of these topic areas, which make up **cell biology**, is fundamental to any biology syllabus as it enables a greater understanding of the physiological processes of living organisms to be achieved.

- All syllabuses expect some knowledge of the structure and properties of biologically important molecules such as **carbohydrates**, **lipids**, **proteins**, **nucleic acids** and **water**. This material should be learnt thoroughly and revised often throughout the entire course, as it will be encountered frequently. Even after the syllabus section or the module in which it is specified has been examined, it is wise to refresh your memory before taking papers on other modules.
- Similarly, it is necessary to have a thorough knowledge of the **structure** of **plant and animal cells** and their **organelles**.
- Most syllabuses specify that the organization of the cells should be studied using **light** and **electron microscopy**, so the use of photographs, drawings and diagrams, as well as your own observations using prepared material, will reinforce your understanding and increase your familiarity with the structures.
- It is important that the **relative sizes** of cells, and of the structures within them, be appreciated, so an understanding of the **scale** or **magnification** of diagrams and photographs is vital.
- All syllabuses require a knowledge of the differences between **eukaryotic** and **prokaryotic** cells, so it is worthwhile tabulating the differences for yourself.
- Similarly, a table, or diagrams, **comparing and contrasting plant and animal cells** would be of value.

Many of the questions set on this area of the syllabus are likely to be straightforward, requiring factual recall. This could involve the identification of organelles in diagrams or photographs of cells, of structures within organelles, a knowledge of the chemical nature and behaviour of particular molecules, or the ability to work out a scale or magnification. Most of these areas would probably be tested in short, structured questions or parts of questions, but you could be asked to write a longer answer covering more of the topic. In the London(EdExcel) module tests, free prose questions carrying 10 marks and, in the synoptic paper, an essay topic carrying 20 marks, would require a more detailed treatment of the topic. In the UCLES Science Biology foundation module test, such a question requiring a longer answer might appear in Section B.

TOPIC OUTLINE

Molecules

A knowledge of the chemical nature and general formulae of biologically significant molecules is necessary in order to understand reactions within cells and the metabolic pathways involved in **cellular respiration**, **photosynthesis** and **protein synthesis**. An understanding of the properties of water and of the structure and significance of carbohydrates, lipids, proteins and nucleic acids is common to all syllabuses, but it is wise to check which specific examples are required.

Water

Water has unusual properties for a molecule of its size and it is vital to all living organisms.

- It is a polar molecule. Hydrogen bonds are formed when the slightly negatively charged oxygen atom at one end attracts the slightly positively charged hydrogen atoms of other water molecules.

  Because of its polarity, it is an excellent solvent for other polar molecules and ionic substances. When dissolved, such substances become more reactive, so water is the ideal medium in which metabolic reactions occur in cells. It is also the transport medium of living organisms, e.g. soluble products of digestion in the blood plasma of vertebrates, sucrose and amino acids in solution in the phloem tissue of flowering plants.
- It has a high heat capacity, i.e. it takes a large amount of heat energy to bring about a small rise in temperature.

  The biological significance of this property is that temperature changes within cells are minimised, providing a stable environment for the enzyme-controlled reactions of metabolism. In addition, where water is a habitat for aquatic organisms, large changes in temperature are avoided.
- It has a high latent heat of vaporisation so that a great deal of heat energy is required to change water from its liquid state to a vapour.

  This is significant in sweating and other methods of temperature control, where heat can be lost from the body, thus cooling it down.
- Its maximum density is at 4 °C. As the temperature gets lower, ice forms, but will float on the surface of the water – a property of significance to aquatic organisms in cold climates.
- It has a high surface tension. Water molecules have a great attraction for one another (cohesion). This plays a role in the movement of water through xylem tissue in flowering plants and in the support of small aquatic organisms.
- In addition, water is an important reactant in hydrolysis reactions, especially those involved in digestion, and in photosynthesis, where it provides hydrogen for reduction.

Carbohydrates

Carbohydrates are organic molecules containing carbon, hydrogen and oxygen. This group of compounds contains:

- **Monosaccharides** – simple sugars with a general formula $(CH_2O)_n$, where *n* is a number from 3 to 9.
- **Disaccharides** – formed from two monosaccharide units which have undergone condensation. A glycosidic bond is formed and a molecule of water removed.
- **Polysaccharides** – composed of large numbers of monosaccharide units linked by glycosidic bonds.

The most common **monosaccharides** are:

- **Trioses**, where $n=3$; triose phosphates are important intermediates in respiration and photosynthesis.
- **Pentoses**, where $n=5$; ribose and deoxyribose are constituents of ribonucleic acid (RNA) and deoxyribonucleic acid (DNA) respectively.
- **Hexoses**, where $n=6$, include glucose, which is the most common respiratory substrate. It exists as α glucose and β glucose, which vary only in the position of H and OH groups on one of the carbon atoms. Other common hexoses are fructose (in fruits and honey) and galactose (in milk).

The most common **disaccharides** are

- **Sucrose** – extracted from sugar cane and sugar beet; the constituent monosaccharides are glucose and fructose.
- **Maltose** – present in malting barley; the constituent monosaccharide is glucose.
- **Lactose** – present in milk; the constituent monosacharides are glucose and galactose.

Polysaccharides are important storage and structural compounds and include:

- **Starch**, which consists of amylose (unbranched chains) and amylopectin (branched chains) of α glucose molecules. It is synthesised by plants and provides a store of energy.
- **Glycogen**, consisting of much-branched chains of α glucose, forms energy stores in animals.

  Both starch and glycogen are suited to their storage function as they are insoluble, compact molecules, which do not interfere with metabolic reactions or alter the osmotic properties of the cells in which they are stored.
- **Cellulose**, made up of long, unbranched chains of β glucose molecules, each chain held to its neighbours by hydrogen bonds. These bundles of chains form microfibrils, which have great tensile strength and play a key role in the structure of plant cell walls.

Lipids

Lipids contain carbon, hydrogen and oxygen, but oxygen content is small. They are **triglycerides** formed by condensation reactions between glycerol and fatty acids. They are:

- non-polar, so insoluble in water
- important as energy stores, yielding more energy on oxidation than carbohydrates
- good heat insulators, provide buoyancy, and form protective cushions around delicate organs in animals.

Phospholipids, which contain a phosphate group, are important components of cell membranes.

Proteins

Proteins are polymers of amino acids. They contain carbon, hydrogen, oxygen and nitrogen, together with sulphur. They have:

- a primary structure, which is the sequence of amino acids joined by peptide bonds to form a polypeptide chain
- a secondary structure, where the polypeptide chain is coiled into an α helix or folded into a β pleated sheet
- a tertiary structure, resulting from further folding, which gives the protein its specific shape.

The helical and tertiary structures are maintained by ionic, hydrogen and disulphide bonds.

Some proteins, such as haemoglobin, have a quaternary structure, involving more than one polypeptide chain.

Proteins can be grouped according to their structure into:

- **Fibrous** proteins, consisting of long parallel chains of polypeptides with little tertiary structure. They form insoluble fibres or sheets and are involved in the structure of **connective tissues**, **tendons**, **bone matrix** and **muscle fibres**.
- **Globular** proteins, with a well-developed tertiary structure. They have spherical shapes, are readily soluble and form **antibodies**, **enzymes**, **hormones** and **plasma proteins**.
- **Conjugated** proteins, which have non-protein (prosthetic) groups associated with them.

Nucleic acids

Nucleic acids make up the genetic material of all living organisms. They are built up of units called **nucleotides** formed by condensation of:

- a 5-carbon sugar, either **ribose** or **deoxyribose**;
- an organic base, either a **purine** (adenine, guanine) or a **pyrimidine** (thymine, cytosine, uracil);
- a phosphate group.

In **ribonucleic acid** (RNA), the sugar is ribose and the nucleotides contain adenine, guanine, cytosine or uracil. In **deoxyribonucleic acid** (DNA), the sugar is deoxyribose and the nucleotides contain adenine, guanine, cytosine or thymine.

Nucleotides are linked together by condensation to form nucleic acids. RNA consists of a single strand and DNA consists of two strands held together by hydrogen bonds between the complementary bases. The chains are anti-parallel and coil round each other forming a double helix.

The role of DNA in cells is to carry the genetic information. It is a constituent of chromosomes and is found in the nucleus of the cell.

Cells and organelles

Cells are the basic units of living organisms. They are aggregated together to form tissues, tissues form organs, organs form part of organ systems and an organism consists of a number of coordinated organ systems.

All **eukaryotic** cells have:

- a **cell surface membrane** (plasma membrane) surrounding the cell contents
- **cytoplasm** in which the cell organelles are situated
- a **nucleus** containing the genetic material in the form of chromosomes
- **mitochondria** in which stages of aerobic respiration occur.

Plant cells differ from animal cells in that they:

- possess **cellulose cell walls** external to the cell surface membrane
- often have a large central **vacuole**
- may contain **starch** grains
- may contain **chloroplasts** in which the process of photosynthesis occurs.

Electron microscopy has enabled the fine structure, or ultrastructure, of cells to be studied and most syllabuses require a knowledge of characteristic features such as the endoplasmic reticulum, ribosomes, Golgi apparatus, mitochondria, nucleus, nuclear envelope, centrioles, microtubules and chloroplasts, together with an understanding of the structure and properties of the cell surface membrane in relation to the fluid mosaic model of its structure.

REVISION ACTIVITY

This activity is designed to help you to learn the various organelles which are present in cells and to summarise the differences between plant and animal cells.

Write the name of each structure on the lines provided and for each structure give a function within the cell.

For the plant cell, underline those structures which are not found in animal cells, and for the animal cell, underline those structures which are not found in plant cells. Check your answers with those on page 68.

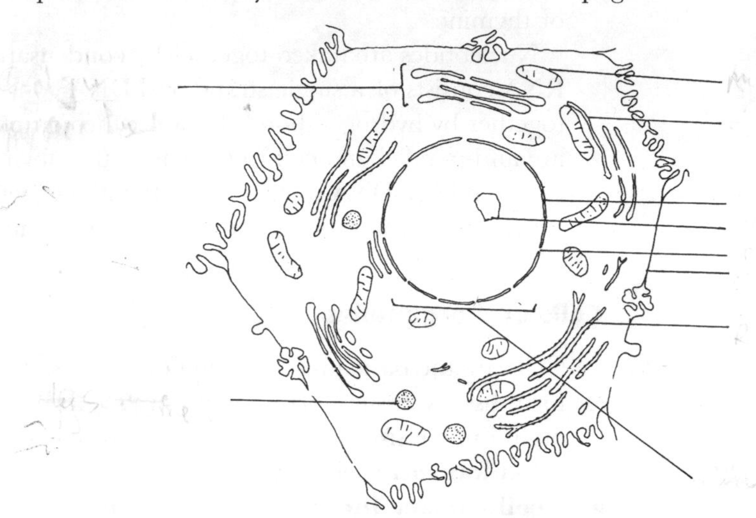

EM drawing of a plant palisade cell with labels to organelles

EM drawing of a liver cell with labels to organelles

EXAMINATION QUESTIONS

Question 1

The table below refers to three organic compounds found in cell organelles. If the compound is found in the organelle, place a tick (✓) in the appropriate box and if the compound is not found in the organelle, place a cross (✗) in the appropriate box.

Organelle	*Phospholipid*	*DNA*	*RNA*
Ribosome			
Chloroplast			
Smooth endoplasmic reticulum			
Mitochondrion			

Total 4 marks

[London]

Question 2

The diagram below shows the structure of part of a molecule of deoxyribonucleic acid (DNA).

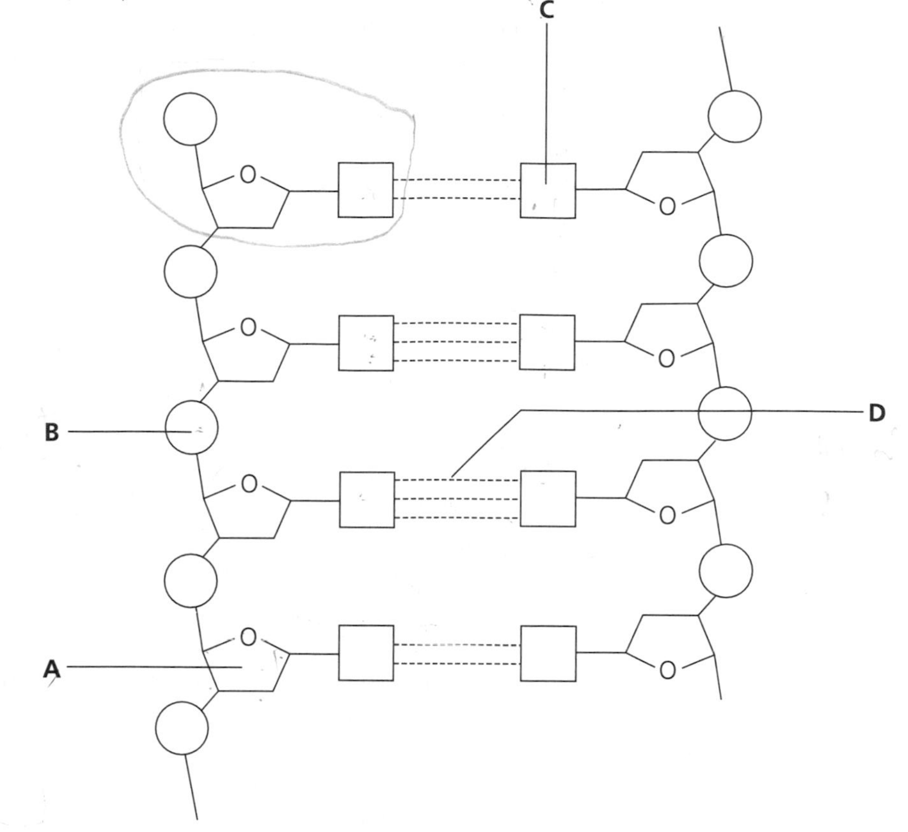

Diagram of part of a DNA molecule

(a) Name the parts labelled A,B,C and D. [4 marks]

(b) (i) On the diagram, draw a ring around *one* nucleotide. [1 mark]

(ii) What type of chemical reaction is involved in the formation of a molecule of DNA from nucleotides? [1 mark]

Total 6 marks

[London]

Question 3

Molecules P, Q and R shown below are important components of living organisms.

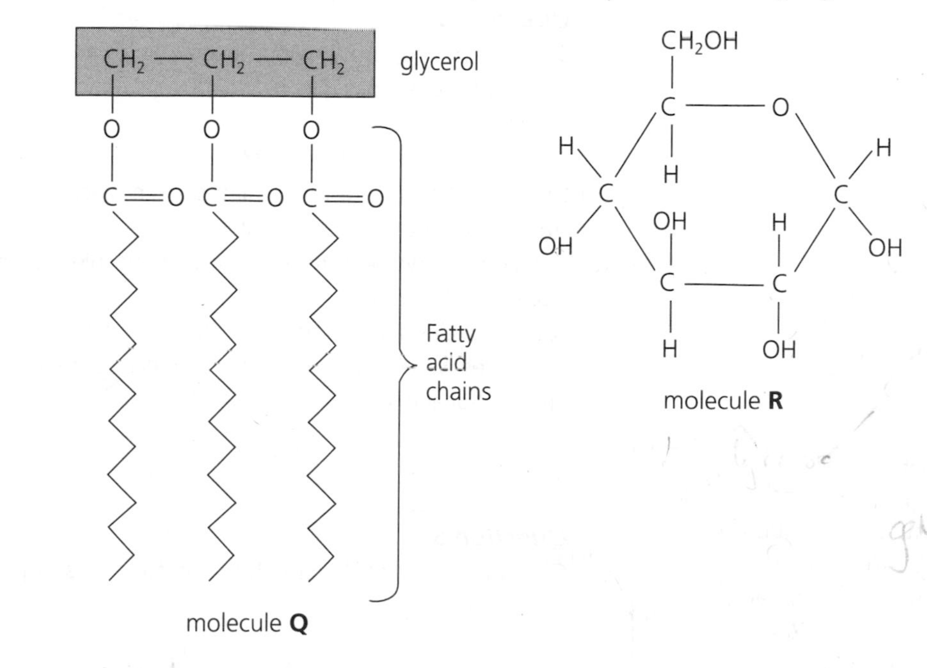

(a) Name
(i) molecules P,Q and R [3 marks]
(ii) *one* element always found in molecule P which would *not* be found in a carbohydrate molecule. [1 mark]
(iii) the type of molecule which would be formed by polymerisation of molecule P. [1 mark]
(iv) the bond which is formed between molecules of P when it polymerises. [1 mark]
(v) the type of molecule which would be formed by polymerisation of molecule R. [1 mark]

(b) Draw a diagram to show how two molecules of R could be joined by a glycosidic bond. Label the glycosidic bond on your diagram. [2 marks]

(c) Describe a test you could carry out to investigate whether a liquid contained
(i) polymers of molecule P [2 marks]
(ii) molecules of Q [2 marks]

Total 13 marks
[UCLES]

Question 4

The table below shows two physical properties of water and ethanol.

Property	***Water***	***Ethanol***
Boiling Point/ °C	100	78
Latent heat of evaporation/10^4 kJ kg^{-1}	226.1	83.9

(a) Briefly explain how the structure and behaviour of the water molecule are responsible for the relatively high values of these two physical properties of water compared with ethanol. [2 marks]

(b) Describe *one* way in which the relatively high latent heat of evaporation of water is important to mammals. [3 marks]

(c) Water has a relatively high specific heat capacity, which means that a large amount of heat energy is required to change its temperature significantly. Outline how this property of water is of importance in the environment of aquatic organisms. [2 marks]

(d) Human blood contains a high percentage of water. State *two* properties of water, not included in the table, which make it suitable as a transport medium in the mammalian blood system. [2 marks]

Total 9 marks
[UCLES]

Question 5

Starch, cellulose, protein and phospholipids all have large molecules.

(a) Which of these molecules is
(i) not a polymer? [1 mark]
(ii) not found in a chloroplast? [1 mark]

(b) Give *one* element present in all protein molecules which is not present in those of starch, cellulose or phospholipids. [1 mark]

(c) Explain how *two* features of a starch molecule are related to its function as a storage carbohydrate. [2 marks]

(d) Some proteins act as hormones. Because of this they are said to be informational molecules. What property of their molecules means that proteins often have informational roles? [1 mark]

Total 6 marks
[NEAB]

Answers to all these questions and to the revision activity can be found on pp. 68–70.
An extra question and Student answer can also be found there.

Question 6

Give an account of the structure and functions of polysaccharides in living organisms.

Total 10 marks
[London]

2 Genetics

REVISION TIPS

There are four main areas on which you need to concentrate in your revision.

1. Be familiar with the specific terms which are used in genetics.
2. Be able to reason logically from the information given to the required answer in solving genetics problems.
3. Have a thorough understanding of the processes and significance of mitosis and meiosis.
4. Be familiar with the genetic code, its manipulation and its application in gene technology.

To help the learning of **genetic terms**, make yourself a set of cards with a term on one side and the definition on the back. Each time you revise genetics, look at a selection of the cards and make sure that you can define each of the terms correctly.

Genetics problems appear on papers set by all the boards and there is no substitute for working your way through problems which have been set on past papers. Get into the habit of showing all your working and making it clear how you progress from one stage to the next. You must learn the definitions for all the terms used in your particular syllabus.

You should be able to draw or to interpret diagrams of the different stages of **mitosis** and **meiosis** and to compare and contrast both the processes and their roles. It is also important to be able to relate the happenings in meiosis to genetic phenomena.

You must make sure that you are familiar with the **genetic code** and methods by which this is manipulated in **gene technology** (genetic engineering).

TOPIC OUTLINE

Genetic terms

These are the terms with which you must be familiar.

- **Gene** A specific length of DNA that codes for one polypeptide.
- **Allele** An alternative form of a gene.
- **Locus** A specific site on a chromosome where a specific gene is found.
- **Dominant allele** An allele that has an effect when it is present.
- **Recessive allele** An allele that only has an effect when an identical pair is present.
- **Co-dominance** Both alleles at a given gene locus are expressed in the phenotype.
- **Homologous chromosomes** A pair of chromosomes of exactly the same length and containing the same gene loci.
- **Homozygote** When the alleles occupying a given locus on homologous chromosomes are identical.
- **Heterozygote** When the alleles occupying a given locus on homologous chromosomes are different.

- **Hemizygote** When the members of a pair of chromosomes are different, for example the XY pair of chromosomes in the human male.
- **Linkage** The occurrence of several genes together on one chromosome.
- **Haploid** A cell containing a single set of chromosomes.
- **Diploid** A cell containing two sets of chromosomes.
- **Polyploid** A cell containing more than two sets of chromosomes.
- **Sex chromosomes** The chromosomes that determine the sex of an individual.
- **Autosomes** The chromosomes in an individual other than the sex chromosomes.
- **Crossing over** The exchange of material between members of a pair of homologous chromosomes during prophase of meiosis I.
- **Chiasmata** Points at which crossing over occurs.
- **Mutation** A change in genetic material. It may be a change in the bases forming a gene (gene or point mutation) or a change in the gross structure of a chromosome (chromosome mutation).
- **Genotype** The genetic make-up of an individual with respect to alleles of one gene.
- **Phenotype** The appearance of an individual resulting from the genotype of the individual and its interaction with the environment in which development occurs.
- **Test cross** Testing the genotype of an individual by mating it with a homozygous recessive.

Basic genetics

- The principle of **segregation** states that of a pair of alleles, only one can be present in a gamete. When two hybrids mate, the theoretical ratio of offspring is 3:1, with 3 showing the dominant phenotype and 1 showing the recessive.
- Some genes have more than two alleles. Such a gene is said to have **multiple alleles**. An individual heterozygous for this gene will contain only two of the possible alleles.
- The principle of **independent assortment** is that either of a pair of alleles can combine with either of another pair.
- A cross involving one pair of alleles is called **monohybrid** inheritance. A cross involving two pairs of alleles is called **dihybrid** inheritance. Such a cross gives a 9:3:3:1 ratio of phenotypes.
- There are various ways in which deviations from the 3:1 or 9:3:3:1 ratios can occur. **Co-dominance** produces a 1:2:1 ratio. **Epistasis** is where a gene at one locus masks the presence of a gene at another. For example, albinism in humans masks all other hair colours. In **polygenic** inheritance, many genes have an additive effect. Environmental effects can affect gene expression. For example, the environmental temperature affects the expression of the himalayan coat colour allele in rodents.
- **Sex determination** is by the presence of sex chromosomes. In humans XX is female and XY is male. Non-disjunction in meiosis gives rise to XO females (Turner's syndrome) and XXY males (Kleinfelter's syndrome).

Gene technology

- Chromosomes can be broken into fragments by **restriction endonucleases**. Each endonuclease cuts DNA at a specific point leaving unpaired bases called **sticky ends**. These can join with other fragments which have complementary sequences of bases.
- Each piece of chromosome is inserted into a host chromosome of a different cell, usually a bacterial cell. This cell, when it divides, will form exact copies of the inserted chromosome fragment.
- Insertion into a bacterium is by a vector, usually a bacterial **plasmid.** Viruses (bacteriophages) are also used. The plasmids contain genes for resistance to antibiotics and so the plasmid-containing cells can be selected.
- The selected bacteria can then be cloned and as they contain the transferred gene they will produce the required protein.
- Useful products such as insulin and growth hormone are produced in this way.
- Genes can also be transferred into other organisms, for example transgenic sheep producing human insulin in their milk.

REVISION ACTIVITY

Aspects of genetics are often tested by the use of genetic problems to be solved. These always give you sufficient information to allow you to reach the answer required. You need to be able to reason logically from the information given. It is essential that you write down all the steps in your reasoning. Sometimes you are asked to answer by means of a genetic diagram. Sometimes you will need to describe the steps in the solution.

Use these questions to practise answering genetics problems.

1. In guinea pigs, black coat colour is dominant to white. A black female guinea pig is test-crossed and produces three offspring in each of three litters, all of which are black. What is her probable genotype?
2. In shorthorn cattle, red coat colour is produced by the genotype RR, roan (a mixture of red and white) by the genotype Rr and white by the genotype rr. If red shorthorns are crossed with roans and the progeny are crossed among themselves to produce a second generation, what proportion of this generation will probably be roan?
3. The ABO blood groups in humans are governed by three alleles. I^A and I^B are co-dominant and I^o is recessive to both I^A and I^B. A man of blood group B is being sued by a woman of blood group A for paternity. The woman's son is blood group O. Could the man be the father of the child? Explain your answer.
4. In *Drosophila* ebony body colour is produced by a recessive allele e and wild type body colour by the dominant allele E. Vestigial wings are produced by a recessive allele vg and normal (wild type) wing size by its dominant allele Vg. If wild type dihybrid flies are crossed and produce 256 progeny, how many of these progeny are expected in each phenotypic class?
5. Male cats may be black or ginger. Females may be black, tortoise-shell or ginger.
   (a) If these colours are governed by a sex-linked locus, how can these results be explained?
   (b) Using appropriate symbols determine the phenotypes expected in the offspring from the cross ginger female x black male.

Check your answers with pp. 71–2.

EXAMINATION QUESTIONS

Question 1

(a) Cell A in the diagram below has two pairs of chromosomes.
Cells B, C and D have each arisen from A by cell division.

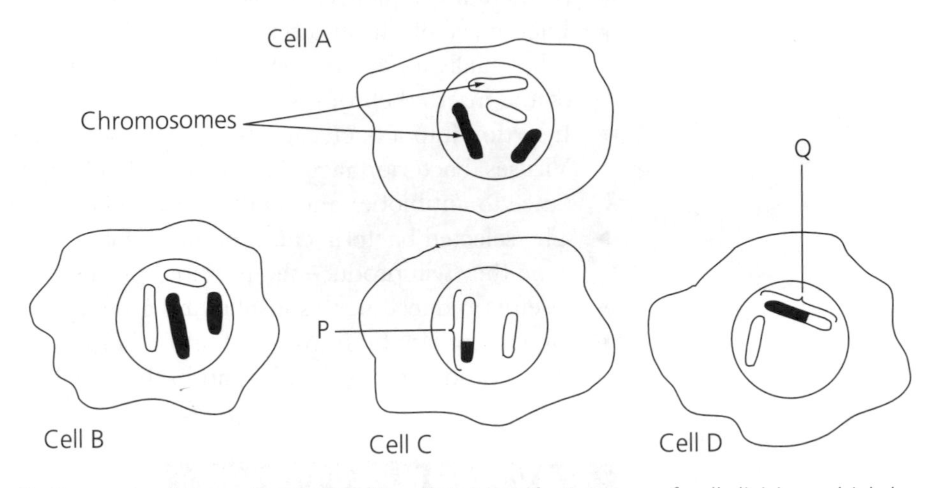

(i) For each of the cells labelled B and C, identify the type of cell division which has occurred to produce the cell. In each case give a reason for your answer.
Cell B
Type of division ....Mitosis..........
Reason ....same no of chromatids..........
Cell C
Type of division ....Meiosis..........
Reason ....chromosome no. halved.......... [2 marks]

(ii) Explain the reasons for the difference between the parts labelled P and Q in cells C and D. Chiasma [3 marks]

(b) State *one* way in which oogenesis differs from spermatogenesis. XX XY [1 mark]

(c) State *two* ways in which embryo development in flowering plants differs from embryo development in humans. [2 marks]

Total 8 marks

[London]

Question 2

(a) A single gene with two alleles controls variation in haemoglobin type in sheep. There are three different phenotypes, corresponding to genotypes S^AS^A, S^AS^B and S^BS^B respectively.
In a flock of sheep the frequency of the allele S^A was found to be 0.6 and the frequency of allele S^B, 0.4.

(i) If the animals mated randomly, what frequencies of allele S^A and allele S^B would be expected in the next generation? [1 mark]

(ii) Using the Hardy-Weinberg equation, calculate the number of sheep with each phenotype in the flock. Show your working. [4 marks]

(b) In humans, the phenotypes and genotypes with respect to the condition of sickle-cell anaemia are as follows:

Phenotype	*Genotype*
Unaffected	$\mathbf{Hb^AHb^A}$
Sickle-cell trait	$\mathbf{Hb^AHb^S}$
Sickle-cell anaemia	$\mathbf{Hb^SHb^S}$

Explain why:

(i) individuals with sickle-cell anaemia may be at a disadvantage. [1 mark]

(ii) The $\mathbf{Hb^S}$ allele remains at a relatively high frequency in many populations. [2 marks]

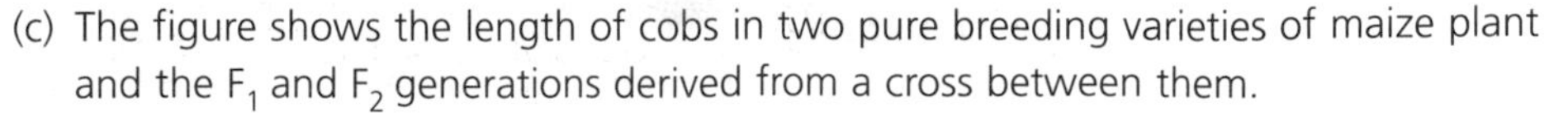

(c) The figure shows the length of cobs in two pure breeding varieties of maize plant and the F_1 and F_2 generations derived from a cross between them.

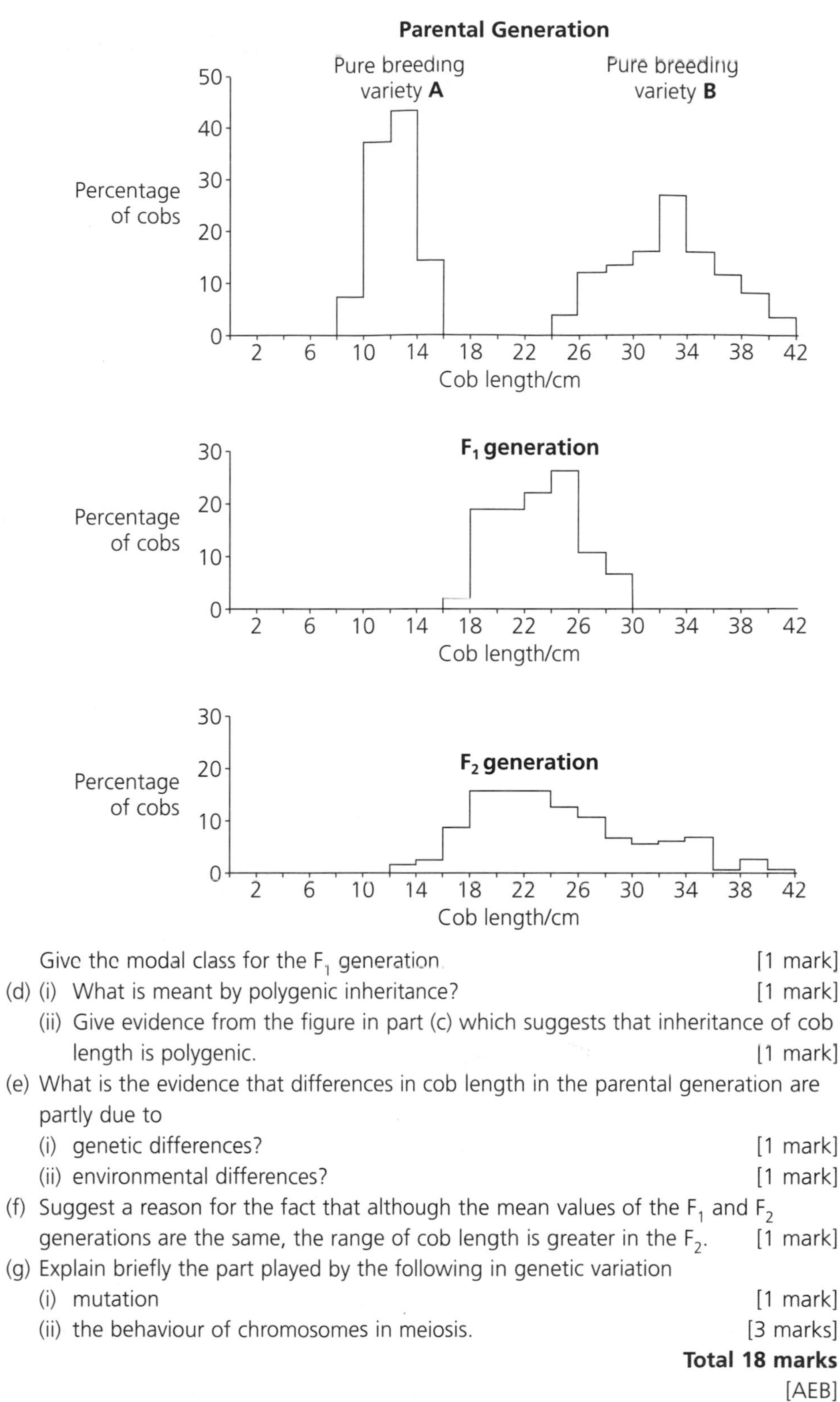

Give the modal class for the F_1 generation. [1 mark]

(d) (i) What is meant by polygenic inheritance? [1 mark]

(ii) Give evidence from the figure in part (c) which suggests that inheritance of cob length is polygenic. [1 mark]

(e) What is the evidence that differences in cob length in the parental generation are partly due to

(i) genetic differences? [1 mark]

(ii) environmental differences? [1 mark]

(f) Suggest a reason for the fact that although the mean values of the F_1 and F_2 generations are the same, the range of cob length is greater in the F_2. [1 mark]

(g) Explain briefly the part played by the following in genetic variation

(i) mutation [1 mark]

(ii) the behaviour of chromosomes in meiosis. [3 marks]

Total 18 marks

[AEB]

Question 3

(a) Complete the table to show which processes occur during the first division of meiosis and those which occur during mitosis. Use a tick (✓) to indicate that the process does occur, and a cross (✗) to indicate that it does not. [3 marks]

Process	*First division of meiosis*	*Mitosis*
homologous chromosomes pair		
crossing over		
chromatids separate		

(b) Explain why mitosis is a suitable type of cell division when tissues are being repaired, but meiosis is not. [3 marks]

Total 6 marks

[UCLES]

Question 4

(a) Give **two** symptoms of Down's syndrome. [2 marks]

(b) The diagram shows the chromosomes of a male with Down's syndrome.

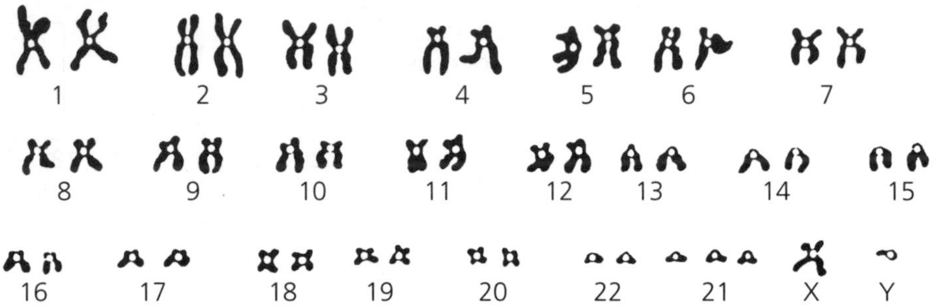

1 2 3 4 5 6 7

8 9 10 11 12 13 14 15

16 17 18 19 20 22 21 X Y

(i) What chromosome abnormality is responsible for Down's syndrome in this male? [1 mark]

(ii) Explain how this abnormality occurs. [3 marks]

(c) The unborn babies of women over 35 years old may be routinely screened for Down's syndrome. Suggest a suitable technique for this purpose. Give a reason for your choice. [2 marks]

Total 8 marks

[NEAB]

Question 5

Thalassaemia is an inherited condition controlled by a single gene with two alleles, the allele for thalassaemia being recessive. It is a disorder which affects the functioning of red blood cells causing anaemia. This condition was common in Cyprus 25 years ago, but since then the incidence has decreased significantly. This decrease resulted from a programme of genetic screening and counselling.

(a) Genetic screening involves testing individuals in the population for the presence of the thalassaemia allele. Which genotype would it be important to identify by this process? Explain your answer. [2 marks]

(b) Explain how genetic counselling might have led to a reduction of the incidence of the disease. [3 marks]

(c) Suggest why it is unlikely that the allele for thalassaemia will be eliminated from the population. [2 marks]

Total 7 marks

[NEAB]

Question 6

The diagram below shows how a genetically modified organism may be produced by inserting a gene from a human into a bacterium.

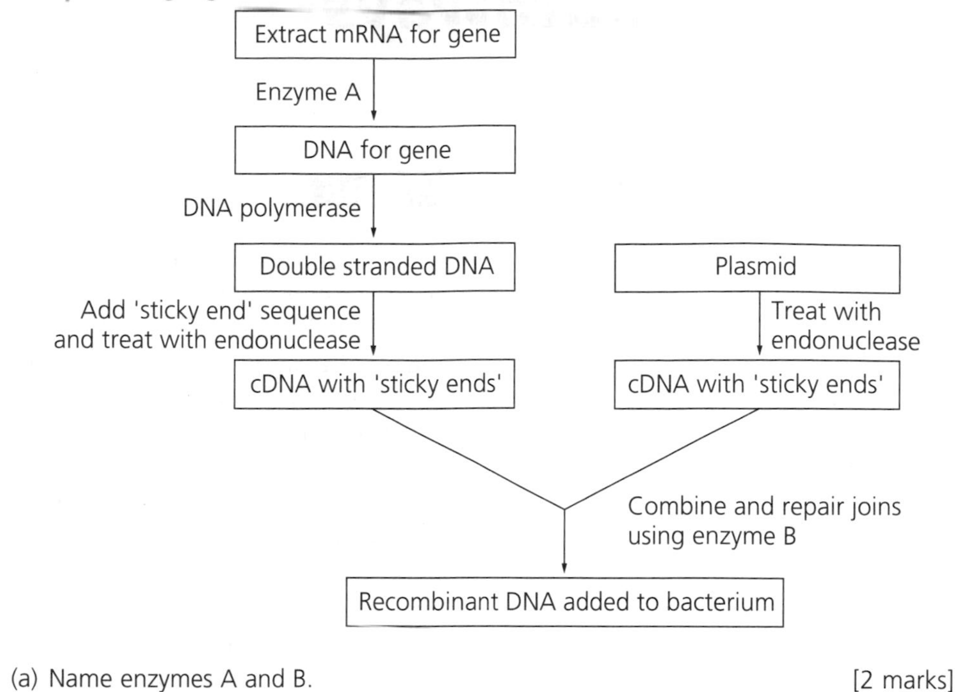

Answers to all these questions and to the revision activity can be found on pp. 71–4.
An extra question and Student answer can also be found there.

(a) Name enzymes A and B. [2 marks]

(b) Describe how treating plasmids with endonuclease produces sticky ends and explain their importance. [3 marks]

(c) Suggest *one* way in which genetically modified organisms may be used. [1 mark]

Total 6 marks

[London]

3 Enzymes and metabolic pathways

REVISION TIPS

Before learning the material in this section of your syllabus, you need to review Chapter 1 to ensure that you have a good understanding of the structure of the relevant biological molecules.

Enzymes are **proteins** and many of their properties are due to their structure. Familiarise yourself with the different groups and the type of reaction that is catalysed, rather than trying to remember the names of specific enzymes.

You will need to be familiar with other groups of compounds, especially **carbohydrates**, as they are involved in **cellular respiration**. In most cases, it will not be necessary to have a very detailed knowledge of every chemical reaction in the pathway, but you should check your syllabus to make certain of what you need to know.

In many syllabuses, the practical work associated with this topic is very clearly specified, so you must make sure that you have done it and that you go through your written accounts when you are revising. You should be clear that you understand the biological background to each practical exercise, know what apparatus was used and how the experiment was carried out. In many enzyme experiments, the effect of varying one factor is investigated, so you should be aware of how other factors (variables) were controlled. Any special precautions needed should also be noted. In the case of experiments using a particular piece of apparatus, such as a simple respirometer, you should be aware of ways in which the apparatus could be adapted to investigate different conditions.

Questions set on this topic can vary enormously: they can involve the straightforward recall of knowledge, the completion of flow charts or diagrams, or be based on the use of a piece of apparatus or an experiment. In longer, structured questions, you may be given data that has to be manipulated in some way, either by plotting a graph or carrying out a simple calculation. Often you may need to apply your biological knowledge to interpret unfamiliar data.

TOPIC OUTLINE

All the metabolic reactions of living organisms take place in a series of steps, each controlled by a specific enzyme. A good knowledge of the structure and functions of enzymes is fundamental to understanding how these metabolic reactions proceed.

Enzymes

Enzymes are

- **globular protein molecules** with a primary, secondary and tertiary structure
- made by living cells

- **catalysts**, speeding up the rate of reactions by lowering the activation energy required
- specific to one type of reaction.

Enzymes are **classified** according to the reactions they catalyse:

- **decarboxylases** – the removal of carbon dioxide
- **dehydrogenases** – the removal of hydrogen atoms
- **hydrolases** – the addition of water or breaking bonds by the addition of water
- **ligases** – the synthesis of new bonds linking two molecules
- **oxidases** – the addition of oxygen to hydrogen
- **transaminases** – the transfer of amino groups
- **transferases** – the transfer of atoms or groups from one molecule to another.

Each enzyme has its own special shape, with an active site to which the substrate molecules bind, forming an **enzyme–substrate** complex. When the reaction occurs, an **enzyme–product** complex results, which then splits releasing the product and the enzyme. Enzymes are specific to one type of reaction because the shape of the active site is complementary to the shape of the substrate molecule (**lock and key hypothesis**), but with some enzymes the active site changes slightly to accommodate the substrate molecule (**induced fit**).

Most enzymes require a non-protein co-factor to be present. This can be:

- an inorganic ion (enzyme activator), e.g. chloride ions increase the activity of salivary amylase
- a prosthetic group – an organic molecule, e.g. haem in the cytochromes which acts as an electron carrier
- a coenzyme, e.g. NAD acts as a link between two different enzyme systems.

Enzyme activity is affected by several factors.

- **Temperature** At low temperatures activity is slow; increase in temperature increases activity, with maximum activity at an optimum. High temperature alters the structure of the molecule (denatures), preventing substrate molecules from binding with the active site.
- **pH** Maximum activity occurs at an optimum pH. Extremes of pH cause the enzyme to denature.
- Substrate concentration.
- Enzyme concentration.
- Presence of **inhibitors** Competitive inhibitor molecules have a similar shape to the substrate and compete for the active site, whereas non-competitive inhibitors either block the active site or change the shape of the enzyme.
- **Accumulation of end-product** End-product inhibition in metabolic pathways is an example of a negative feedback mechanism preventing the accumulation of a metabolite.

Metabolic pathways

Metabolism is the term used to describe all the chemical reactions that occur within the cells of living organisms. Those reactions which involve the synthesis, or building up, of compounds are called **anabolic** and those where compounds are broken down are called **catabolic**. Anabolic reactions require energy, they are endergonic, whereas catabolic reactions often result in the release of energy.

Many of the reactions in **cellular respiration** involve the oxidation of a substrate by the removal of hydrogen atoms or electrons. **Nicotinamide adenine dinucleotide** (NAD^+) is an electron carrier (or hydrogen carrier) which accepts hydrogen atoms and electrons, becoming reduced ($NADH + H^+$). These electrons are passed along a chain of carriers at different energy levels, eventually combining with oxygen to form water. Sufficient energy is made available to synthesize molecules of **adenosine triphosphate** (ATP) from adenosine diphosphate (ADP) and inorganic phosphate (P_i), a process known as **oxidative phosphorylation**.

ATP provides the necessary energy for activities such as:

- synthesis of compounds (anabolism)
- active transport
- muscle contraction
- nerve transmission.

When ATP is hydrolysed to ADP and P_i, large amounts of energy are released.

Respiration occurs in every living cell and is the only way in which cells can obtain energy for their activities. It is **aerobic** if it requires oxygen and **anaerobic** if it takes place in the absence of oxygen, or if oxygen is not utilised.

In aerobic respiration, when a molecule of glucose (carbohydrate substrate) is oxidised to carbon dioxide and water, the total amount of energy released is 2800 kJ. The breakdown occurs in two stages:

1. the glucose is broken down to pyruvic acid in glycolysis
2. the pyruvic acid enters a mitochondrion, is converted to acetyl coenzyme A, which then becomes incorporated into a cycle of reactions (Krebs cycle) during which carbon dioxide and hydrogen atoms are removed.

During **glycolysis**:

- two molecules of ATP are used to phosphorylate the glucose molecule, thus making it more reactive
- the phosphorylated sugar splits into two molecules of triose phosphate (3C sugars)
- triose phosphate is converted to pyruvic acid
- four molecules of ATP are produced and four hydrogen atoms are removed
- the hydrogen atoms are accepted by the hydrogen acceptor molecule (hydrogen carrier) NAD^+.

During the **Krebs cycle**:

- acetyl coenzyme A combines with oxaloacetate (4C) to form citrate (6C)
- citrate is converted back to oxaloacetate in a series of steps during which one molecule of ATP is synthesised, two molecules of carbon dioxide and eight hydrogen atoms are removed
- the hydrogen atoms are accepted by NAD^+ or another electron carrier FAD^+ (flavin adenine dinucleotide) and undergo oxidative phosphorylation. The removal of hydrogen atoms is under the influence of dehydrogenase enzymes. For each pair of hydrogen atoms accepted by NAD^+ and passed along the chain of electron carriers, three molecules of ATP are synthesized. If FAD^+ is the acceptor, then two molecules of ATP result.

The reactions of glycolysis take place in the **cytoplasm** of the respiring cells, but the other reactions occur in the **mitochondria**. The reactions of the Krebs cycle occur in the **matrix** and the electron carriers span the **inner mitochondrial membranes**.

Anaerobic respiration takes place in the absence of oxygen, so the electron transport chain does not function. The initial stages are similar to aerobic respiration in that glycolysis takes place and the respiratory substrate is broken down to pyruvate. Some reduced NAD is formed, which is re-oxidised, so that glycolysis can continue.

Anaerobic respiration occurs in some bacteria and in yeast when deprived of oxygen.

In yeast:

- pyruvate is converted to acetaldehyde (ethanal) by removal of carbon dioxide (decarboxylation)
- acetaldehyde is reduced by $NADH + H^+$ to give ethanol and NAD^+.

This process is also known as **fermentation** and is used in the brewing of beer and wine-making.

During periods of physical exertion, anaerobic respiration can occur in muscle tissue. The pyruvate is reduced to lactate, using hydrogen from NADH + H^+. The lactate accumulates in the muscle and is oxidised back to pyruvate when sufficient oxygen becomes available.

REVISION ACTIVITY

1 (a) Define the term 'enzyme
(b) Give three characteristics of enzymes

2 Give the functions of the following groups of enzymes:
decarboxylases
dehydrogenases
hydrolases
ligases
oxidases
transaminases
transferases

3 Name three types of co-factor required by enzymes

4 Name three factors which affect enzyme activity

5 Give three functions of ATP

6 (a) Distinguish between aerobic and anaerobic respiration
(b) Describe two situations where anaerobic respiration is found in living organisms

EXAMINATION QUESTIONS

Question 1

Read through the following passage about respiration, then write on the dotted lines the most appropriate word or words to complete the account.

Respiration is the process by which organisms can release energy from organic compounds. In living cells, ... respiration can be divided into several stages. Glycolysis takes place in the .... of the cell. Glycolysis produces the compound .... which enters the next stage, the .... cycle. This compound is broken down releasing .... and .... and energy in the form of heat and ATP.

Total 6 marks

[London]

Question 2

The diagram outlines the pathway of anaerobic respiration in muscle tissue.

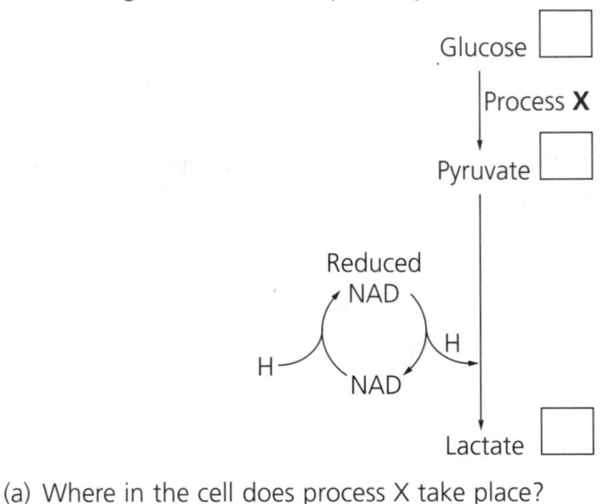

(a) Where in the cell does process X take place? [1 mark]

(b) From which process in the cell does the hydrogen come that reduces the NAD? [1 mark]

(c) Complete the boxes in the diagram to show the number of carbon atoms present. [1 mark]

(d) During process X there is a net gain of ATP. Why is the term *net gain* used? [2 marks]

Total 5 marks

[AEB]

Question 3

(a) Explain the meaning of the term enzyme. [3 marks]

Thrombin is a protein-digesting enzyme which is produced in blood plasma when tissues are damaged. Thrombin catalyses the hydrolysis of four peptide bonds in the soluble globular protein fibrinogen, converting it to the insoluble fibrous protein fibrin. Fibrin precipitates out from the plasma, forming a tangle of fibres in which blood cells become trapped, forming a clot.

(b) Outline the differences in structure between a fibrous protein and a globular protein, explaining how these differences affect their solubility. [4 marks]

Leeches are parasites which feed by sucking blood. When they bite, they secrete saliva into the wound. The saliva contains a protein called hirudin. The hirudin occupies the active site of thrombin, where it links to the thrombin by forming hydrogen bonds.

(c) Suggest how the secretion of hirudin helps a leech to feed more efficiently, and explain how this effect is brought about. [4 marks]

Total 11 marks

[UCLES]

Question 4

The diagram shows a simple respirometer. It is being used to measure the rate of oxygen uptake by a suspension of yeast cells in tube A. There are no yeast cells in tube B. A muslin bag containing soda lime is suspended in each tube. The syringe in tube B can be used to level the fluid in the manometer.

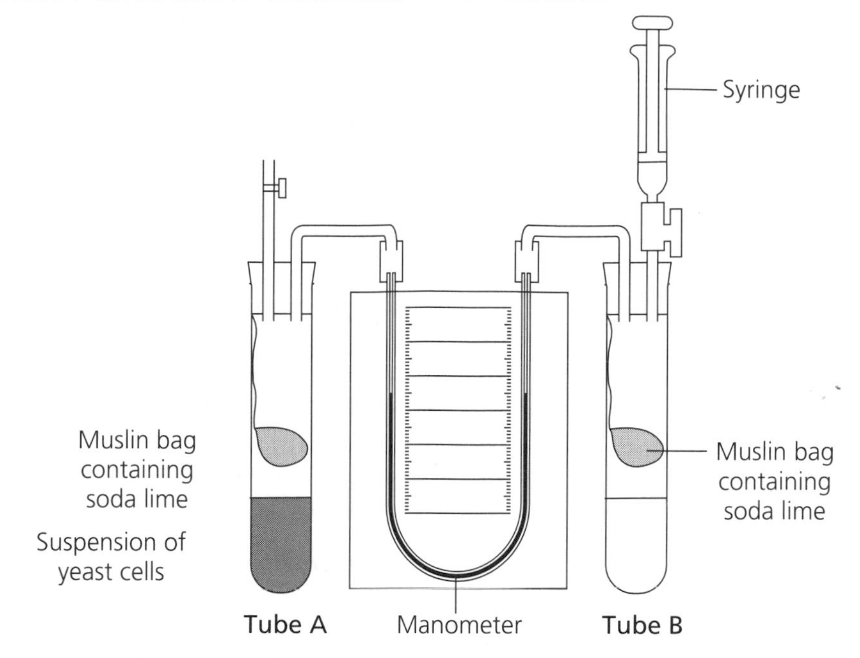

Source: adapted from M.J. ROWLAND, *Biology* (Nelson) 1992

(a) (i) What is the purpose of the soda lime in tube A? [1 mark]
(ii) Explain how tube B acts as an experimental control. [2 marks]
(b) The table shows the readings that were obtained over a period of 50 minutes.

Time/minutes	***Syringe reading/mm³***
0	0
10	3.1
20	5.9
30	9.2
40	12.1
50	14.9

Use these readings to calculate the respiratory rate of the yeast suspension. Show your working. [2 marks]

Total 5 marks

[AEB]

Question 5

(a) Outline the processes which occur in respiration during
(i) glycolysis [6 marks]
(ii) the Krebs cycle [6 marks]
(b) Describe the ways in which the structure of a mitochondrion enables aerobic respiration to occur efficiently. [6 marks]

Total 18 marks

[UCLES]

Question 6

The diagram below summarizes a procedure for isolating cell components. Cells, such as liver cells, are homogenized (broken up) and then spun in a centrifuge at increasing speeds. At each stage, the pellet is retained and the supernatant (liquid) is then centrifuged at a higher speed. The figures show the centrifugal forces produced as the number of times they are greater than the force of gravity, *g*.

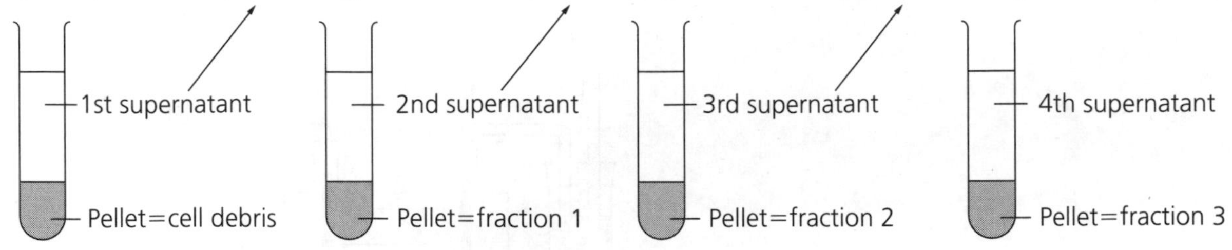

(a) One of the fractions contains mitochondria, another contains nuclei and another contains ribosomes.

(i) Identify the fraction in which each of the components is found. Write your answers in the table below.

Component	***Fraction number***
Mitochondria	
Nuclei	
Ribosomes	

[2 marks]

(ii) Explain the reasoning for your answer in (i). [2 marks]

(b) One of the three fractions contains the enzyme succinic dehydrogenase. The activity of this enzyme can be demonstrated using methylene blue or tetrazolium chloride (TTC) with succinic acid as the substrate.

(i) Describe a method you could use to determine which of the three fractions contains succinic dehydrogenase. [4 marks]

(ii) Which of the three fractions would show dehydrogenase activity? [1 mark]

(c) State *two* components, other than water, that would be found in the 4th supernatant. [2 marks]

Total 11 marks

[London]

Answers to all these questions and to the revision activity can be found on pp. 75–8.
An extra question and Student answer can also be found there.

4 Nutrition

REVISION TIPS

This topic covers a range of activities of living organisms concerned with acquiring food and shows the dependence of heterotrophic organisms on green plants as producers. In order to gain a full understanding of the topic you will need to have knowledge of the structure of enzymes and their role in controlling metabolic pathways and of the structure of carbohydrates, fats and proteins.

All syllabuses require a basic knowledge of the process of **photosynthesis**, but you should check to see exactly how much detail is required, so that you do not learn unnecessary complex reactions. It is wisest to learn a simple pathway first and then to add details as you begin to understand the processes, rather than trying to learn all the details at the first attempt. Again, building up a simple flow chart of your own is a good way of testing yourself and of fixing the details in your memory. Remember that photosynthesis does not stop at the formation of starch, so it would be wise to check your syllabus to see if you need to know any details of the synthesis of amino acids and lipids.

A knowledge of **heterotrophic nutrition** will include reference to mammals, but you should be familiar with **saprobiontic** (saprotrophic) and **parasitic** nutrition as well as **mutualistic behaviour**.

There is much practical work associated with this area of any biology syllabus. With respect to photosynthesis, there are several basic experiments. These involve investigation of the effects of different environmental factors on the rate, together with chromatography of the chloroplast pigments. Experiments involving the enzymes associated with heterotrophic nutrition are also appropriate to this topic.

A knowledge of flowering plant structure, especially leaves, is often required, so it is wise to remind yourself of the anatomical features associated with the uptake of the raw materials of photosynthesis.

Some syllabuses also require details of the histology of the alimentary canal of mammals and the structure of teeth.

Questions on this topic will range from straightforward recall of knowledge, such as completing pathways, naming organs and defining terms, to data-handling, use of apparatus and experimental design. You should be prepared to draw on your knowledge of other syllabus sections, particularly with respect to enzyme action.

TOPIC OUTLINE

All living organisms require a source of food to provide them with:

- materials for growth
- energy for metabolic processes.

Some organisms can synthesise their own food requirements and are known as **autotrophic**, whereas others, the **heterotrophic** organisms, need to be supplied with ready-made organic compounds.

There are four main types of heterotrophic nutrition:

1 **Holozoic** Typical of higher animals such as mammals.
2 **Saprobiontic/saprotrophic** Organisms feed on dead and decaying organic matter.
3 **Parasitic** One organism obtains its food from another living organism, the host, which suffers in some way.
4 **Mutualistic** This is sometimes known as **symbiosis** and involves two organisms living in a close association, where both benefit from the relationship.

Autotrophic nutrition

Autotrophic organisms can synthesise their own food requirements, building up complex organic molecules from simple inorganic ones. In order to achieve this they need a source of energy. There are two types of autotrophic nutrition:

1 **Photosynthesis** Green plants, algae and certain types of bacteria build up complex organic molecules from carbon dioxide, water and mineral ions using light energy.
2 **Chemosynthesis** A few groups of bacteria are able to synthesise organic molecules using inorganic sources of carbon and chemical energy derived from special methods of respiration.

The process of photosynthesis can be summarised by the following general equation:

$$CO_2 + H_2O \rightarrow (CH_2O)_n + O_2$$

$$\text{carbon dioxide} + \text{water} \xrightarrow[\text{chlorophyll}]{\text{light}} \text{carbohydrate} + \text{oxygen}$$

Carbon dioxide is obtained from the atmosphere by diffusion through the stomata of the leaf. The concentration of carbon dioxide in the atmosphere is greater than that in the leaf, so a concentration gradient exists.

Water is obtained from the soil via the roots and is transported to the leaves in the xylem tissues of the root, stem and petioles to the leaf lamina.

Mineral ions, which are required for the synthesis of amino acids and other organic compounds, are also taken up from the soil and are transported in solution in the xylem.

Green plants must be able to absorb light energy and take in carbon dioxide gas and water from their surroundings. Other synthetic processes follow from the availability of simple organic molecules and energy: the synthesis of amino acids occurs, and these are built up into proteins, and also of fatty acids and glycerol (needed for the production of lipids).

Green plants contain **photosynthetic pigments** to absorb light energy. These pigments are located on the membranes in the **chloroplasts**. Chloroplasts are most abundant in the cells of the palisade mesophyll of leaves, but they also occur in the spongy tissue of the leaf and in the outer cortex of young stems. The pigments present are:

- the **chlorophylls**, a and b, which are green and absorb light in the red and blue-violet regions of the spectrum
- the **carotenoids**, which are yellow-orange and also absorb blue-violet light.

Light is essential for photosynthesis, a fact which can be demonstrated easily by keeping a plant in darkness for 48 hours and testing a leaf for the presence of starch.

The **light intensity** is important in determining the rate of photosynthesis. Increasing the light intensity increases the rate of photosynthesis up to a critical point at which another factor becomes limiting, i.e. any further increase in light intensity does not increase the rate.

The **wavelength** of light is also important, as chlorophyll only absorbs red and blue-violet light, reflecting the green. This can be demonstrated by an **absorption spectrum**, where the absorbance of light by the pigments is plotted against wavelength. An **action spectrum**, which is a graph showing the amount of photosynthesis at different wavelengths of light, can be compared with the absorption spectrum for chlorophyll and shows that the peaks coincide: there is maximum photosynthesis at those wavelengths which are absorbed.

Photosynthesis occurs in two stages:

1 the **light-dependent stage**, requiring light energy and resulting in the production of ATP (adenosine triphosphate) and NADPH (reduced nicotinamide adenine dinucleotide phosphate);
2 the **light-independent stage**, in which the NADPH is used to reduce carbon dioxide to carbohydrate, using ATP as an energy source.

In the **light-dependent** reactions, which take place in the **grana** of the chloroplasts, water is split and ATP molecules are formed during photophosphorylation. The pigment molecules are organised into two **photosystems**, Photosystem I (PSI) and Photosystem II (PSII). In each photosystem, there are two types of photosynthetic pigments:

1 primary pigments, which are specialised forms of chlorophyll a
2 accessory pigments, which include all the other forms of chlorophyll.

The **accessory pigments** absorb light energy and pass their energy on to the **primary pigments**, which then emit electrons causing the light-dependent reactions to occur.

When light is absorbed, the energy is passed on to the primary pigment molecules which emit high energy electrons. These are taken up by electron acceptors and passed along a chain of electron carriers in a series of oxidation-reduction (redox) reactions. Each carrier is at a lower energy level than the one before it, so sufficient energy is released to build up molecules of ATP from ADP and P_i. This process is known as **photophosphorylation**.

In **cyclic photophosphorylation**, only PSI is involved and only ATP is formed.

In **non-cyclic photophosphorylation**, light is absorbed by PSII and PSI, ATP molecules are built up and hydrogen from the splitting of water is used to reduce $NADP^+$ to $NADPH + H^+$.

The **light-independent** reactions take place in the **stroma** of the chloroplast. Carbon dioxide combines with a carbon dioxide acceptor molecule, ribulose 1,3 bisphosphate (RUBP).

In this carboxylation, catalysed by ribulose bisphosphate carboxylase, two molecules of glycerate-3-phosphate are formed. The glycerate-3-phosphate is phosphorylated, using ATP, then reduced to glyceraldehyde-3-phosphate, using NADPH. This sequence of enzyme-controlled events is referred to as the **Calvin cycle**. The resulting glyceraldehyde-3-phosphate is used to regenerate the RUBP and to build up carbohydrates and other complex organic molecules.

The **rate** at which photosynthesis occurs is affected by environmental factors:

- **light intensity** – the higher the light intensity the faster the rate
- **carbon dioxide concentration** – usually the limiting factor, as the carbon dioxide concentration in the atmosphere is about 0.035 per cent
- **temperature** – affects the enzyme-controlled reactions of the light-independent stage, so an increase in temperature will increase the rate up to a critical point.

Plants in which the first products of photosynthesis are 3 carbon compounds such as glycerate-3-phosphate are termed C_3 plants. In some tropical plants, such as maize and sugar cane, it has been shown that the first products of photosynthesis are 4 carbon compounds. These plants are called C_4 plants. The leaves have a slightly different internal anatomy and photosynthesis is more efficient in hotter, dryer climates.

In addition to carbon dioxide and water, green plants require 13 other essential elements in order to grow successfully. These elements are taken up as ions and the most important are:

- **nitrates** for the synthesis of amino acids, proteins, nucleic acids, pigment molecules and coenzymes
- **phosphates** for the synthesis of nucleic acids, phospholipids and ATP
- **magnesium** for the synthesis of chlorophyll molecules and as an enzyme activator.

Heterotrophic nutrition

All heterotrophic organisms need to obtain complex organic compounds such as carbohydrates, lipids and proteins to provide them with the materials for growth and with a source of energy. In addition, their diet should include mineral ions, vitamins and water. Vitamins and mineral ions are only needed in small amounts but contribute to the formation of essential coenzymes and co-factors in metabolic reactions.

In **holozoic nutrition**, five stages can be recognized:

1. **Ingestion** Food is taken in.
2. **Digestion** The complex organic compounds are hydrolysed to simpler, soluble molecules: hydrolysis is speeded up by digestive enzymes such as carbohydrases, proteases and lipases.
3. **Absorption** The simpler, soluble products of digestion are taken into the circulatory system.
4. **Assimilation** The products of digestion are incorporated into the body and used.
5. **Egestion** Any undigested parts of the food are eliminated.

These five stages can be recognised in most animals, but most syllabuses refer to **mammals**, where there is a long, tubular structure, the alimentary canal or gut, with associated glands such as the liver and the pancreas.

Food is taken into the mouth, where the teeth break up large masses or lumps of food. There are three types of **teeth** in mammals:

1. **incisors** at the front for cutting and biting;
2. **canines** at the side for gripping and holding;
3. **cheek teeth**, the **premolars** and **molars**, for crushing, grinding, chewing and slicing.

The teeth of many groups of mammals are highly adapted to their diet, e.g. herbivores have ridged cheek teeth for dealing with vegetation, and the teeth of carnivores are specialised for catching prey and eating flesh.

During chewing, the food is mixed with **saliva**, a watery secretion from the salivary glands, which contains **amylase**, a digestive enzyme speeding up the hydrolysis of starch to maltose.

The food is swallowed and conveyed to the **stomach** via the oesophagus by peristaltic contractions of the longitudinal and circular muscles.

The presence of food in the mouth stimulates the **gastric glands** in the stomach to secrete the **gastric juice**, which contains:

- **pepsin** – a protease which speeds up the digestion of proteins by hydrolysing peptide bonds
- **rennin** – present in young mammals, this enzyme coagulates the soluble protein in milk

- **hydrochloric acid** – activates the proteases, which are secreted in an inactive form; provides the correct pH for their action; and kills off pathogenic micro-organisms in food.

In the stomach, the food is churned up and thoroughly mixed by the muscular action. When it has reached a semi-liquid state, called **chyme**, periodic relaxation of the pyloric sphincter releases it into the duodenum, where it is mixed with:

- bile from the gall bladder
- pancreatic juice from the pancreas.

Bile contains bile salts that emulsify fats into tiny droplets.

Pancreatic juice contains:

- **pancreatic amylase** which speeds up the hydrolysis of any remaining starch to maltose
- **pancreatic lipase** which speeds up the hydrolysis of lipids to fatty acids and glycerol
- **trypsin**, a protease, which is activated by enterokinase and continues the hydrolysis of proteins
- **alkaline salts** which help to neutralize the acidity of the chyme.

In the duodenum and ileum, there are **enzymes** located on the membranes of the microvilli of the epithelial mucosa. These include:

- **maltase** which hydrolyses maltose to glucose
- **sucrase** which hydrolyses sucrose to glucose and fructose
- **endopeptidases** and **exopeptidases** which complete the hydrolysis of proteins to amino acids.

Secretion of the digestive juices into the duodenum and ileum is controlled by **hormones**. The presence of acid food in the duodenum triggers the production of:

- **secretin** causing the liver to secrete bile and the pancreas to produce the components of the pancreatic juice
- **CCK-PZ** (cholecystokinin-pancreozymin) which stimulates enzyme release from the pancreas and the release of bile from the gall bladder.

Absorption of the soluble products of digestion occurs mainly from the duodenum and the ileum, which make up the **small intestine**. Several features of this region of the gut contribute to the efficiency of absorption.

- It has a large surface area due to its length, the presence of villi and of microvilli on the columnar epithelial cells.
- Contraction and relaxation of the smooth muscle fibres in the villi enable mixing of the contents and bring the epithelial cells into contact with the digested food.
- There is an extensive capillary network in the villi for transport of the absorbed products of digestion.
- It has lacteals for the absorption of lipids.

Glucose and **amino acids** are absorbed across the epithelium of the villi by a combination of diffusion and active transport, passing into the capillary network of the villi and thence to the **liver** via the **hepatic portal vein**.

Fatty acids and **glycerol** molecules diffuse into the epithelial cells and recombine to form **lipids** which then pass into the lacteals of the villi. Here they become coated with **proteins** to form **chylomicrons**, which eventually pass into the blood from the lymph.

Vitamins and mineral ions do not undergo digestion and are absorbed from the small intestine.

Water is absorbed from the colon.

REVISION ACTIVITY

Read through the following passage on photosynthesis and fill in the blank spaces. You should read the whole passage through first, before attempting to fill in the answers. Check your answers with p. 78

There are four pigments commonly found in the chloroplasts of higher plants; chlorophyll a, chlorophyll b, ...(i) and ....(ii). Chlorophyll a absorbs mainly ....(iii) and ....(iv) light. The absorption of light causes the displacement of an ....(v) from the chlorophyll a molecule. This may be passed back to the chlorophyll via a series of ....(vi) which are at a progressively lower ....(vii) level. Coupled with this transfer is the synthesis of ....(viii). This compound may subsequently be used in the light-independent reactions of photosynthesis which occur in the ....(ix) region of the ....(x). During non-cyclic ....(xi), the displaced ....(xii) is combined with ....(xiii) ions resulting from the ....(xiv) of water to form reduced ....(xv), which is used in the ....(xvi) cycle to convert ....(xvii) to glyceraldehyde 3-phosphate. This can be converted to ....(xviii) which is the acceptor molecule for carbon dioxide or to ....(xix), which can be used in respiration or converted to ....(xx) and stored.

EXAMINATION QUESTIONS

Question 1

The diagram below shows part of the light-independent pathway of photosynthesis.

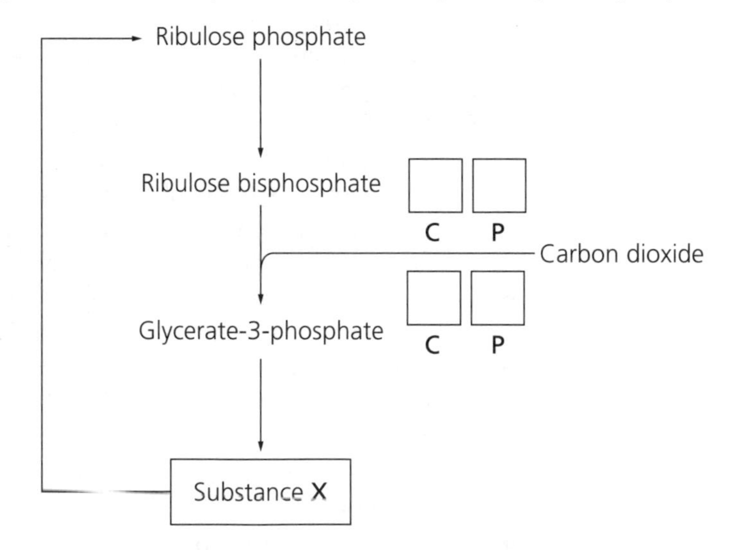

(a) For the two compounds, ribulose bisphosphate and glycerate-3-phosphate, enter the number of carbon atoms in each molecule in the boxes labelled C and the number of phosphate groups in the boxes labelled P. [1 mark]

(b) Give the name of substance X. [1 mark]

(c) Give *two* specific roles of ATP in the light-independent pathway of photosynthesis. [2 marks]

Total 4 marks

[AEB]

Question 2

The diagram below shows the structure of a chloroplast as seen using the electron microscope.

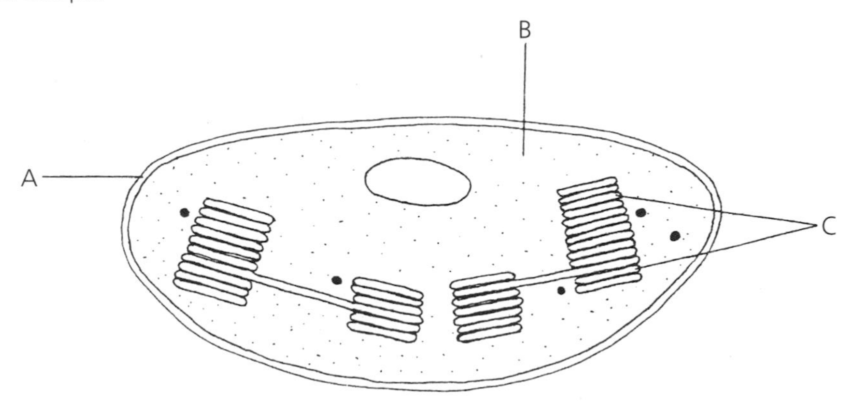

(a) Name the parts labelled A, B and C. [3 marks]

(b) The actual length of this chloroplast is 2.5 μm. Calculate the magnification of this diagram. Show your working. [2 marks]

Total 5 marks

[London]

Question 3

The graph shows the rate of photosynthesis in two crop plants, A and B, at different light intensities.

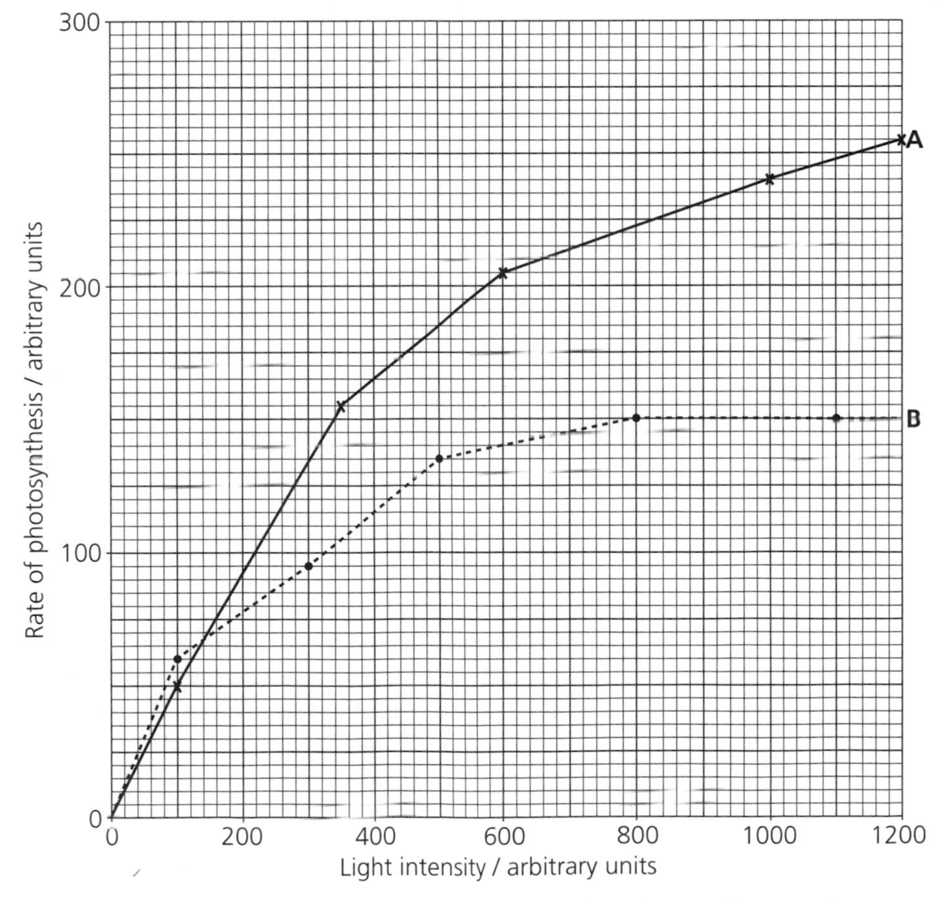

(a) Describe the ways in which increasing light intensity has similar effects on the two crops. [2 marks]

(b) Suggest the most likely limiting factor for crop B at a light intensity of
  (i) 100 arbitrary units
  (ii) 1000 arbitrary units [2 marks]

(c) From these data suggest, with reasons, which crop is better suited for growth in tropical conditions. [2 marks]

Total 6 marks

[NEAB]

Question 4

The diagram shows how protein can be digested in the human gut.

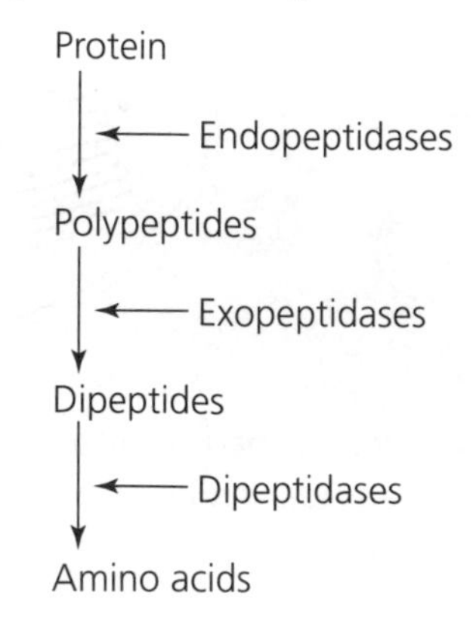

(a) (i) Describe the main difference between the mode of action of an endopeptidase and an exopeptidase. [1 mark]

(ii) Give the name of the endopeptidase produced by the pancreas. [1 mark]

(b) Where precisely is the site of action of dipeptidases in the small intestine? [1 mark]

(c) Ruminants such as cattle need considerable quantities of protein yet they can survive on diets which contain very little. Explain how they obtain the extra protein that they need. [2 marks]

Total 5 marks

[AEB]

Question 5

(a) Large food molecules are usually digested in a number of steps, by more than one enzyme. An example of this is the digestion of protein in humans.

(i) Complete the table.

Enzyme	***Substrate***	***Product***
Endopeptidase		Polypeptides
Exopeptidase	Polypeptides	

[2 marks]

(ii) Suggest why the combined actions of these two enzymes are more efficient than exopeptidase on its own. [1 mark]

(b) A series of experiments concerning gall bladder function were carried out with human volunteers. One group was given a drug, loxiglumide, in salt solution intravenously. As a control, a second group was given just a salt solution. Ten minutes after starting, volunteers were given a fat-rich meal. The volume of the gall bladder was measured at regular intervals using ultrasound. The results are shown on the graph.

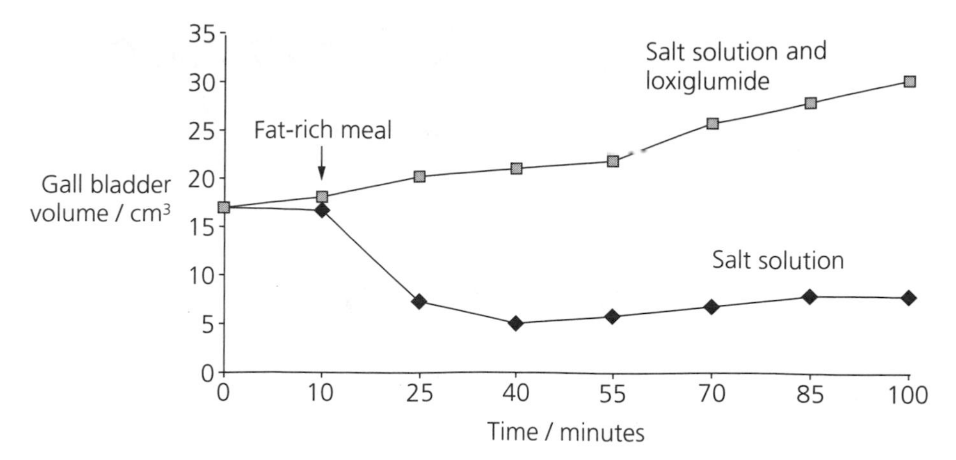

(i) Why was the control group given salt solution? [1 mark]

(ii) Use the data in the graph to describe the effect of loxiglumide on gall bladder activity. [2 marks]

(iii) Suggest how taking the drug loxiglumide might affect the digestion of the fat-rich meal. [2 marks]

(c) Suggest an explanation for the effect of loxiglumide on the emptying of the gall bladder. [1 mark]

Total 9 marks

[NEAB]

Question 6

(a) Describe the ways in which a dicotyledonous leaf is adapted to carry out photosynthesis efficiently. [10 marks]

(b) (i) Explain, with the aid of suitable examples, what is meant by the term *limiting factor* in photosynthesis. [5 marks]

(ii) Suggest how a gardener could use a greenhouse to produce more favourable conditions for photosynthesis. [3 marks]

Total 18 marks

[UCLES]

Answers to all these questions and to the revision activity can be found on pp. 78–81.
An extra question and Student answer can also be found there.

5 Ecosystems and the environment

REVISION TIPS

There are three main areas that need to be firmly in your mind and which should be revised carefully.

1 You need to be familiar with and be able to define clearly the main ecological terms.
2 You need to know the relationships of the animals, plants and abiotic factors in the ecosystem or ecosystems that are specified in your particular syllabus.
3 You need to be able to specify and describe the use of ecological procedures for studying populations, communities and the various abiotic factors.

Make yourself a set of cards with a term on one side and the definition on the back. Each time you revise ecology, look at a selection of terms and make sure that you can define each of them correctly. When you are revising ecological techniques, make sure that you are confident about the use of each. For example, know what sort of investigation quadrats are appropriate for and when you would use a transect rather than random quadrats.

TOPIC OUTLINE

Ecological terms

- **Population** A group of organisms of a single species occupying a particular area.
- **Community** The sum total of interacting populations in an area.
- **Ecosystem** A community of organisms which together with their physical environment form a self-perpetuating ecological unit.
- **Habitat** The particular area occupied by a population.
- **Biotic factors** The sum total of the organisms within a habitat and their interactions.
- **Abiotic factors** The physical factors influencing the organisms. They are divided into two different types. **Edaphic** features relate to the soil and include all its physical and chemical characteristics. **Climatic** features include light, temperature, moisture, salinity and, particularly, the stability or variability of these.
- **Microhabitats** Areas of varying characteristics within a habitat.
- **Ecological niche** The place of each species within an ecosystem. This is not only the space that it occupies, but the role it carries out within the community and its interrelationships with other species.
- **Environmental resistance** The environmental factors reducing the growth of a population.
- **Carrying capacity** The population level of a species at which there is zero population growth. As a population nears the carrying capacity, the environmental resistance increases.
- **Food chain** The sequence from plant (producer) to herbivore to primary and secondary carnivores. As most herbivores (primary consumers) and carnivores (secondary and tertiary consumers) usually feed on more than one species, simple food chains rarely exist.

- **Food web** Interconnecting food chains giving a more realistic picture of feeding relationships within an ecosystem.
- **Trophic level** One stage in a food chain, e.g. autotrophs are the first trophic level.
- **Pyramid of numbers** A pyramid that shows the number of organisms at each trophic level.
- **Pyramid of biomass** This represents the total biomass at each successive trophic level.
- **Pyramid of energy** Represents the total energy content of each successive trophic level. There are large losses of energy between each pair of trophic levels. This loss of energy limits the number of trophic levels in any ecosystem.

Energy flow and biogeochemical cycles

Energy enters ecosystems via **photosynthesis** or **chemosynthesis** and is fixed in the form of organic compounds. Energy is passed to heterotrophs when these compounds are eaten. Energy is not recycled within an ecosystem, so constant new supplies of energy are needed to maintain an ecosystem.

The **nitrogen cycle** is the cycling of inorganic and organic nitrogen within an ecosystem. The main processes involved are the following:

- **Putrefaction** Decay processes converting organic nitrogen to ammonia.
- **Nitrification** The conversion of ammonia via nitrites to nitrates.
- **Nitrogen fixation** The conversion of atmospheric nitrogen to nitrogen compounds by free living prokaryotes such as *Clostridium* or *Anabaena* or by symbiotic bacteria (*Rhizobium*) and mycorrhizal fungi.
- **Denitrification** The loss of nitrogen in anaerobic conditions by the conversion of nitrates to molecular nitrogen.

The **carbon cycle** is the cycle of the fixation of **carbon dioxide** by photosynthesis or chemosynthesis to produce organic compounds, and the loss of carbon by the production of carbon dioxide in **respiration.**

Sulphur and **phosphorus** are also recycled, being fixed in organic compounds during anabolism and returned to inorganic compounds during decay.

Human effects on the environment

- Human activities produce a wide variety of **pollutants** of land, air and water.
- The major air pollutants are **carbon dioxide** which is an important compound in relation to **global warming**, **sulphur dioxide** which is largely responsible for **acid rain** and **oxides of nitrogen** which irritate lungs and, along with **hydrocarbons** from vehicle exhausts, are responsible for **photochemical smog**.
- The major water pollutants are **nitrates** and **phosphates** from the excessive use of inorganic fertilizers, sewage, animal wastes and organic wastes from industry.
- **Eutrophication** is the natural ageing of a freshwater lake. The process is speeded up by nitrate and phosphate pollution. The increased growth of aquatic plants is followed by a rise in the **biochemical oxygen demand** when these plants die and decay.
- Human activities bring about **desertification** on a small or large scale by monoculture and by overgrazing.
- **Conservation** broadly equates with the management of biological and physical resources and the maintenance of natural habitats. It may entail destructive processes such as culling, or burning areas of gorse or bracken. It may entail total neglect to allow climax communities to develop. It may

also mean change in land use, replanting of natural plants, or the reintroduction of species which have become extinct in the area.

REVISION ACTIVITY

1 From your field notebook, make a list of the organisms you recorded in one ecosystem which you have studied. Construct a food web incorporating these organisms.

2 (a) Construct pyramids of numbers
   (i) where the producers are small but found in large numbers
   (ii) for a woodland ecosystem where the producer is a small number of large plants.

(b) Construct a pyramid of energy using the following data.

producers $144\,000$ kJ m^{-2} yr^{-1}
herbivores 2600 kJ m^{-2} yr^{-1}
primary carnivores 250 kJ m^{-2} yr^{-1}
secondary carnivores 2 kJ m^{-2} yr^{-1}

Check your answers with p. 82.

EXAMINATION QUESTIONS

Question 1

The table shows the ratios of biomass between successive trophic levels in a number of grassland ecosystems.

Ecosystem	***Biomass ratio***	
	Producer/ Primary consumer	***Primary consumer/ Secondary consumer***
Bunchgrass	1984	2
Tallgrass	1376	18
Southern shortgrass	2071	7
Northern shortgrass	1657	4

From this table it can be seen, for example that in the bunchgrass system, 1984 units of producer biomass are required to yield 1 unit of primary consumer biomass.

(a) How many units of producer biomass are required to yield 1 unit of secondary consumer biomass in the northern shortgrass ecosystem? Show your working. [2 marks]

(b) Which of the ratios shown in the table represents the most efficient conversion of biomass? [1 mark]

(c) (i) Explain why it is not possible to have a ratio of 1 in this table. [1 mark]

(ii) Suggest **one** explanation for the fact that the figures in the second column of the table are much larger than those in the third column. [1 mark]

Total 5 marks

[AEB]

Question 2

Notonecta, a water boatman, is an insect about 1.5 cm long, which swims on its back. It feeds on animals often much larger than itself, such as tadpoles and small fish, but it will also eat other insects.

A group of students estimated the population of *Notonecta* in a pond using the mark, release and recapture method.

(a) (i) What would be the most suitable apparatus for capturing *Notonecta*? [1 mark]

(ii) Explain precisely how *Notonecta* should be marked so that they could be recognised on recapture. [2 marks]

(b) These were the students' results.

Number of *Notonecta* captured, marked and released on day 1	Number of *Notonecta* captured on day 2	
	marked	*unmarked*
50	12	42

Calculate the estimated size of the population of *Notonecta* in the pond. Show your working. [2 marks]

(c) In a separate investigation lasting several years, it was found that the mean population of *Notonecta* in the pond never rose above 400.
Suggest **two** density-dependent factors which could account for this maximum population size in the pond and explain how each factor has its effect. [4 marks]

Total 9 marks

[NEAB]

Question 3

The Norfolk Broads (large areas of fresh water) have become heavily contaminated with phosphate over the last 100 years. The drawings show the effect this has had on the community of plants and animals which live there.

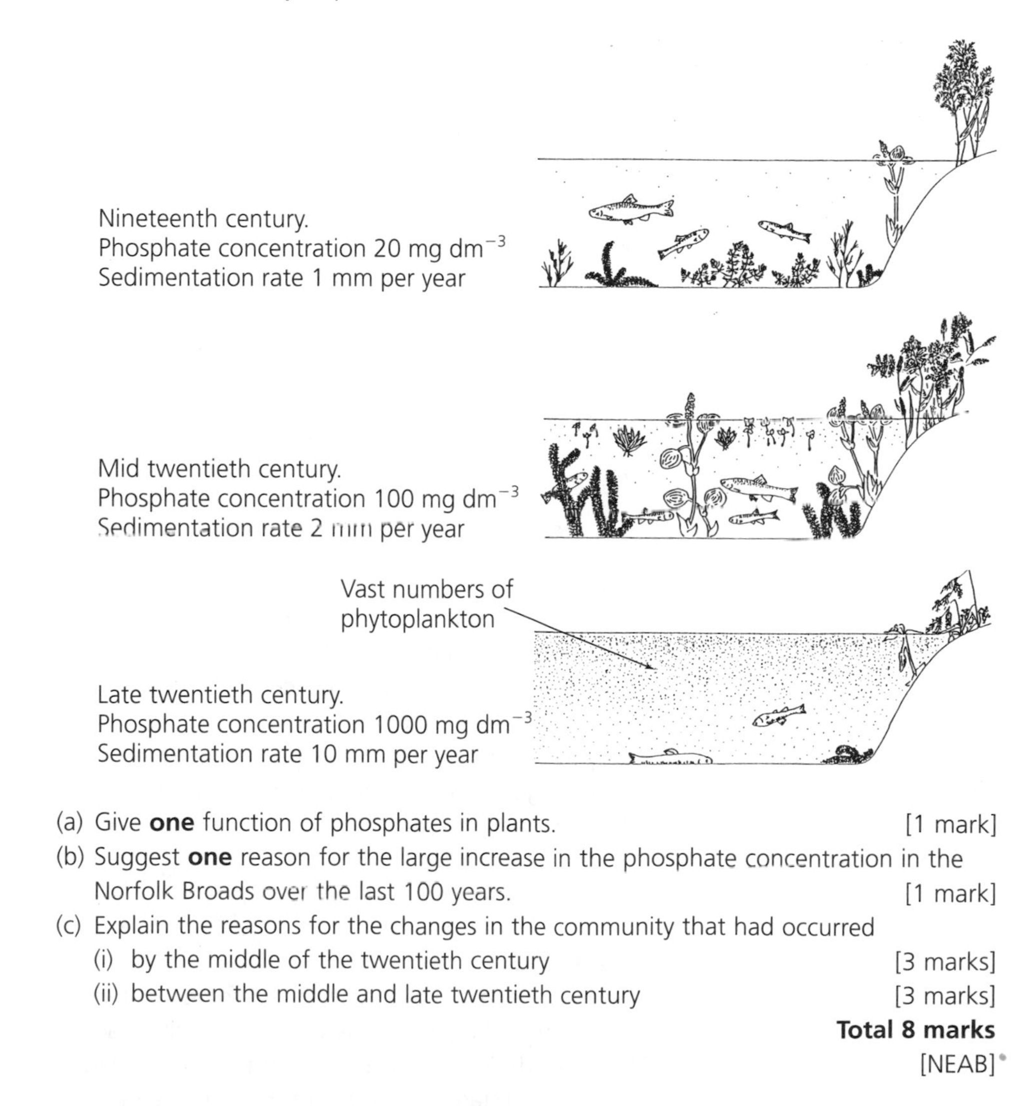

(a) Give **one** function of phosphates in plants. [1 mark]

(b) Suggest **one** reason for the large increase in the phosphate concentration in the Norfolk Broads over the last 100 years. [1 mark]

(c) Explain the reasons for the changes in the community that had occurred

(i) by the middle of the twentieth century [3 marks]

(ii) between the middle and late twentieth century [3 marks]

Total 8 marks

[NEAB]*

Question 4

(a) The treatment of sewage produces semi-solid material called sludge. Sludge contains high concentrations of nitrogen compounds, including nitrate and ammonia. The disposal of sludge is a problem for water companies, as they cannot simply dump it into waterways.
Explain why the dumping of sludge into waterways would cause environmental damage. [4 marks]

(b) One method of disposing of sludge is to apply it to agricultural land, where the sludge supplies fixed nitrogen to crops.
 (i) Explain the meaning of the term *fixed nitrogen*. [1 mark]
 (ii) Why do growing crops require a supply of fixed nitrogen? [1 mark]

(c) Research has been carried out into the rate of leaching of nitrate from grassland to which sludge has been applied. The sludge was applied to two similar areas of grassland. In one area, it was spread on the surface, while in the other area it was injected into the soil to a depth of 70 cm.
The rate of leaching was measured by taking samples of water flowing through the soil, and measuring the concentration of nitrate in them. This was done on several occasions, after different amounts of rainfall.
The graph below shows concentrations of nitrate in the water flowing through the soil, plotted against rainfall, for the two methods of sludge application.

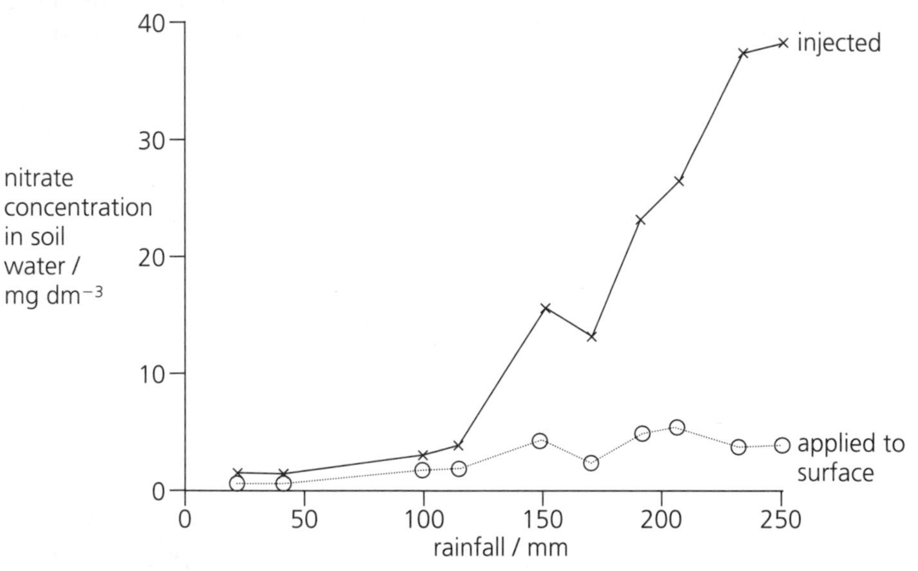

Source: Institute of Grassland & Environmental Research, 1992 Report, AFRC Grassland & Environmental Research, 1993

 (i) Using the information in the graph, describe the relationship between the leaching of soil nitrate and rainfall. [2 marks]
 (ii) Describe, and suggest an explanation for, the difference between the amount of leaching when sludge is applied to the surface, compared with sludge applied by injection into the soil. [4 marks]

(d) Using the information in the graph, suggest how and when a farmer should apply sludge to grassland, in order to minimise pollution of waterways by leaching of nitrate through the soil. [2 marks]

Total 14 marks

[UCLES]

Question 5

A student noticed that the density of some plant species appeared to differ depending on how far the plants were from the main road.
The mean density (plants per m^2) of three plant species A, B and C was measured at different distances from the main road. The mean density of the same three plant species was also determined at the side of a narrower secondary road in the same locality.

The results of the investigations are shown in the diagrams below.

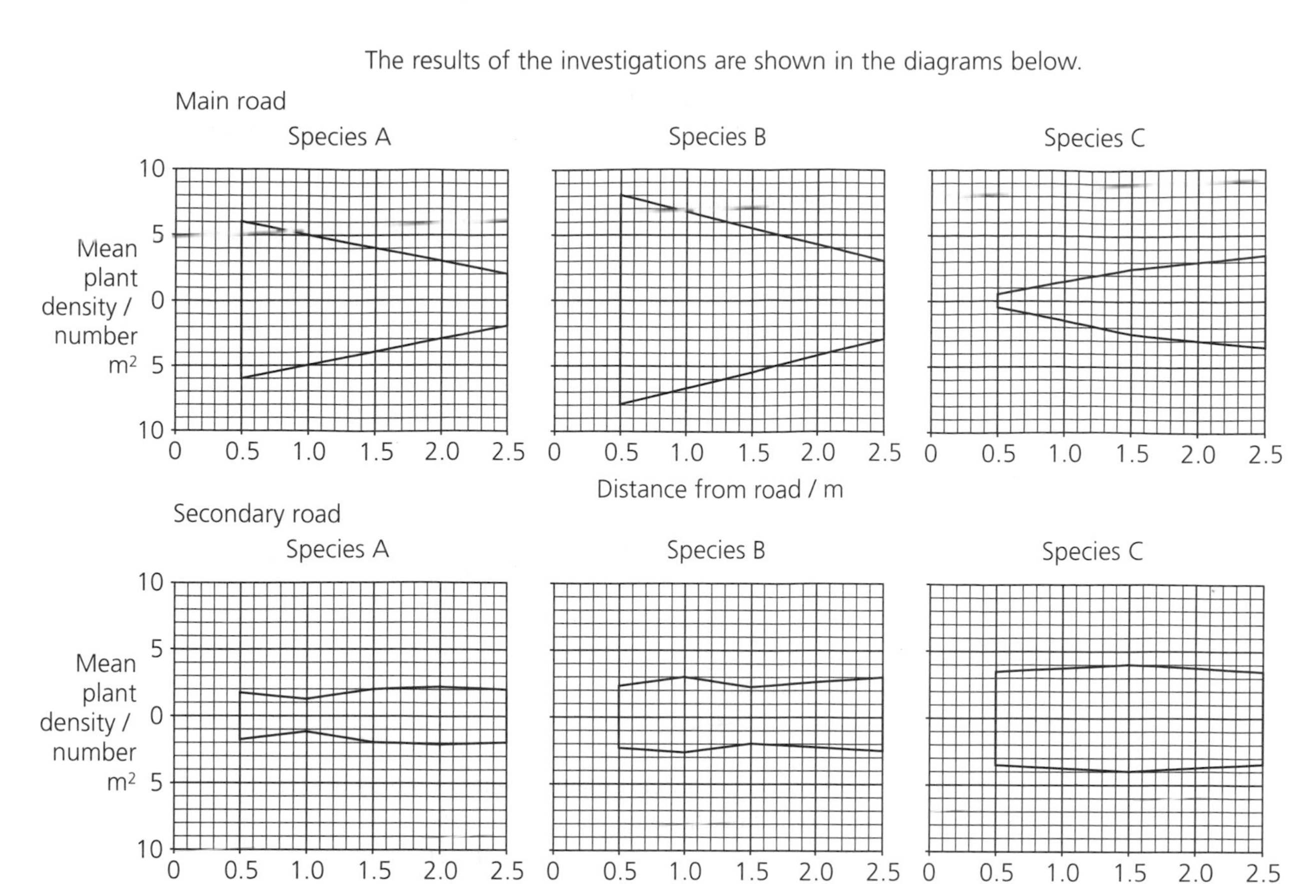

(a) Describe a procedure the student could have used to determine the mean density of the three plant species. [4 marks]

(b) (i) Comment on the relationships between plant density and the distance from the main and secondary road for species A and B. [4 marks]

(ii) Comment on the ways in which the distribution of plant species C differs from that of plant species A. [2 marks]

(c) In addition to determining the plant densities, the student measured the pH of soil samples taken at the same distance from each road.
The result is shown in the graph below.

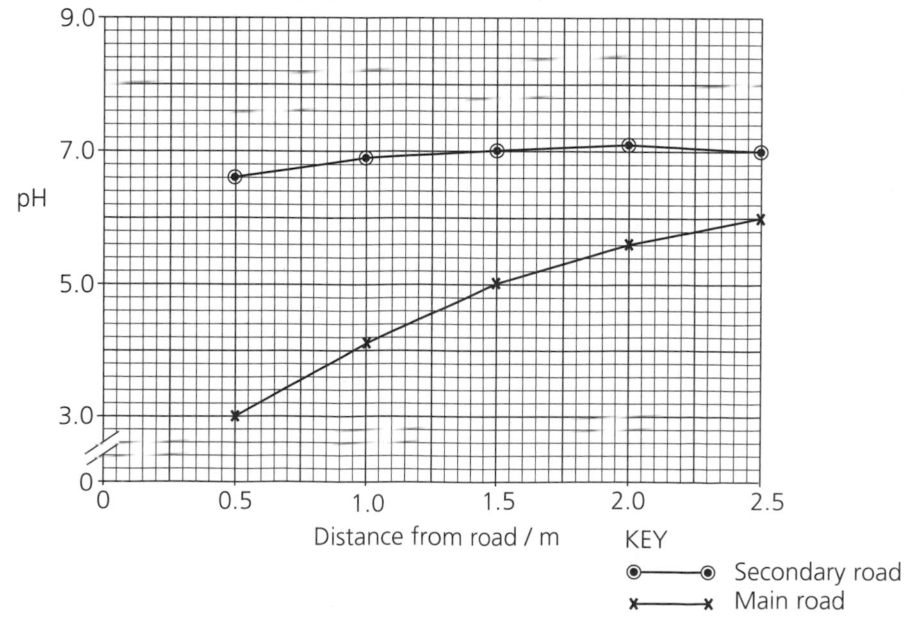

(i) Suggest an explanation for the differences between the pH of the soil at the side of the main road and the pH at the side of the secondary road. [2 marks]

(ii) Using the data given for pH, suggest an explanation for the distribution of the three species A, B and C. [2 marks]

(iii) Suggest *one* factor, other than pH which could account for the differences in density distribution of the plant species at the side of the main road. [1 mark]

Total 15 marks

[London]

Question 6

The diagram below shows some of the processes involved in the cycling of nitrogen in an ecosystem.

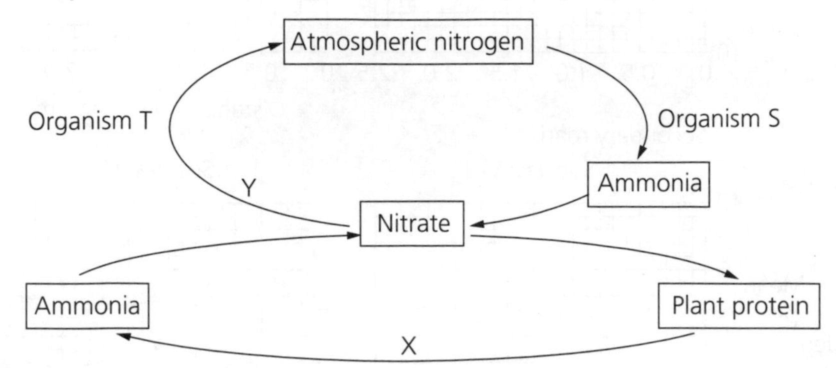

(a) (i) State the genus of *one* organism represented by the letter S and *one* organism represented by the letter T in the diagram. [2 marks]

(ii) Name the processes represented by the arrows X and Y. [2 marks]

(b) Explain how excessive use of nitrate fertilisers might lead to eutrophication of a lake. [3 marks]

Total 7 marks

[London]

Answers to all these questions and to the revision activity can be found on pp. 82–6.
An extra question and Student answer can also be found there.

6 Reproduction and development

REVISION TIPS

All the syllabuses include reproduction in mammals and flowering plants. Refer to your syllabus to find out if you also need to know about reproduction in lower animals and plants.

Questions about reproduction and development may include sections referring to meiosis and/or mitosis, so revise these along with reproduction.

A number of hormones play important roles in mammals and various growth substances are important in the development of flowering plants. As with genetic and ecological terms, you may find that revision cards are a help in learning and remembering the roles of these. You may also find cards useful in remembering details of life cycles of lower plants.

Check with your own syllabus for the level of detail needed about embryonic development in both mammals and flowering plants. Make sure that you know the exact meaning of any terms used in the syllabus.

TOPIC OUTLINE

Reproduction in mammals

- The male reproductive system consists of the **testes** which produce **spermatozoa** and **testosterone**, the **penis** and the genital ducts and accessory glands which connect the two.
- Spermatozoa are produced in the **seminiferous tubules** and are stored and mature in the **epididymis**.
- Testosterone controls male secondary sexual characteristics.
- The female reproductive system consists of **ovaries** which produce **ova** and female hormones, a muscular **uterus** in which the embryos develop and the **vagina** connecting it with the outside. The **oviducts** (**Fallopian tubes**) conduct ova to the uterus. Various accessory organs are involved in producing vaginal fluids and in sexual stimulation.
- **Oogenesis** differs from **spermatogenesis** in that only one ovum is produced from each primary oocyte as opposed to four spermatozoa from each primary spermatocyte. Also oogenesis occurs in the embryo whilst spermatogenesis occurs after puberty.
- **Oestrus** is the cyclical release of ova. In humans the **menstrual cycle** is superimposed on the oestrus cycle. The cycles are controlled by gonadotrophic hormones, **follicle stimulating hormone** (FSH) and **luteinizing hormone** (LH) from the pituitary gland and **oestrogen** and **progesterone** produced in the ovaries.
- Once an ovum is released the ruptured **Graafian follicle** forms the **corpus luteum** which produces progesterone. If the ovum is fertilised, this remains.
- Fertilisation occurs when a sperm cell enters the egg cell. This is facilitated by the **acrosome reaction**. The acrosome membrane ruptures and enzymes are produced which digest the outer membranes of the egg cell.

- After sperm entry, the egg cell nucleus completes the second meiotic division and the male and female **pronuclei** fuse to form the **zygote**.

Development of a mammalian embryo

- The fertilised egg cell divides by a series of mitotic divisions, **cleavage**.
- A solid ball of cells, a **morula**, is formed. A cavity, **blastocoel**, appears in this, forming a hollow ball of cells, a **blastocyst**. Cells continue to be formed and migrate inwards to form a new cavity.
- As a result of this migration the three germ layers, **ectoderm**, **mesoderm** and **endoderm** are laid down.
- The ectoderm gives rise to the skin and nervous system. The mesoderm forms muscle, bone, blood system, kidneys and sex organs. The endoderm forms the gut (except for the pharynx and rectum, which are ectodermal), part of the lungs and accessory organs of the gut.
- As the embryo develops, four embryonic membranes are formed.
- The yolk sac forms the **trophoblastic villi** which grow into and absorb nutriment from the uterine wall.
- The **amnion** and **chorion** arise as a fold around the edges of the embryonic disc. The cavity between these two layers forms the **extra-embryonic coelom**. The chorion forms **chorionic villi** which burrow into the uterine wall.
- The **allantois** grows out from the developing hind gut. Around the tail of the embryo, it fuses with the chorion to form the **allanto-chorion** which gives rise to the embryonic part of the **placenta**.
- At birth when levels of progesterone fall, **prolactin** stimulates the breasts to produce milk. **Oxytocin** stimulates the release of milk from the nipple.

Sexual reproduction in flowering plants

- The **stamens** form the **androecium** or male part of a flower.
- The **carpels** form the **gynaecium** or female part of a flower. The carpels consist of the **ovary**, **style** and **stigma**.
- These reproductory organs are surrounded by the **perianth** formed by the **sepals** and **petals**.
- A stamen is made up of a **filament** and an **anther**. The anther contains four **pollen sacs**. Each pollen sac contains **microspore mother cells**. Each mother cell undergoes meiosis to produce four **pollen grains**. The **generative nucleus** in the pollen grain represents the **male gametophyte** which will produce two **male gamete nuclei**.
- Each carpel contains one or more **ovules**. Each ovule develops from a **nucellus**. At its apex, a **megaspore mother cell** undergoes meiosis to form four **megaspores**. One develops to form an **embryo sac** containing eight haploid nuclei. The embryo sac represents the female **gametophyte**. One nucleus becomes the **female gamete** with a **synergid** on either side. A group of three nuclei at the opposite end form the **antipodal cells**. The remaining two nuclei remain in the centre of the embryo sac and are called **polar nuclei**.
- **Pollination** is the transfer of pollen from anther to stigma. Flowers are specialised for pollination by insects or wind.
- Pollination leads to **fertilisation**. In flowering plants there is **double fertilisation**. One male nucleus fuses with the egg cell nucleus, the other fuses with the polar nuclei to form the triploid **endosperm** nucleus.
- The fertilised ovule develops into a seed with an embryo consisting of **cotyledon(s)**, **radicle** and **plumule**.

- Usually after a period of dormancy, the seed **germinates**. A suitable temperature, moisture, oxygen and sometimes light are needed. Water is absorbed rapidly, the tissues swell and enzymes are mobilised under the influence of **gibberellin**.
- Growth includes **cell expansion** and **cell differentiation**. Growth occurs in the **meristems** at the stem and root apices and in the cambium.

Asexual reproduction

- Protoctists reproduce by **binary fission**.
- Bryophytes and pteridophytes have an asexual spore-producing phase, the **spermatophyte**, and a sexual stage, the **gametophyte**, in their life cycles.
- Many flowering plants produce **propagules** by mitotic division. These may be modified stems, roots or leaves. Runners, rhizomes, suckers, tubers and bulbils are common forms and give rise to **vegetative propagation**.
- **Bulbs** are formed from the swollen **leaf bases** of stems and **corms** from the swollen **stem bases**. Lateral buds may produce subsidiary bulbs or corms which can grow independently. These structures are therefore involved in **perennation** and vegetative propagation.
- Artificial vegetative propagation can be carried out by taking **cuttings**, by **budding** or by **grafting**.

REVISION ACTIVITY

1 Without reference to textbooks or your notes, make a list of the hormones involved in mammalian reproduction and give the roles of each of them.

2 Label the diagram below and on it indicate the area where the placenta will develop.

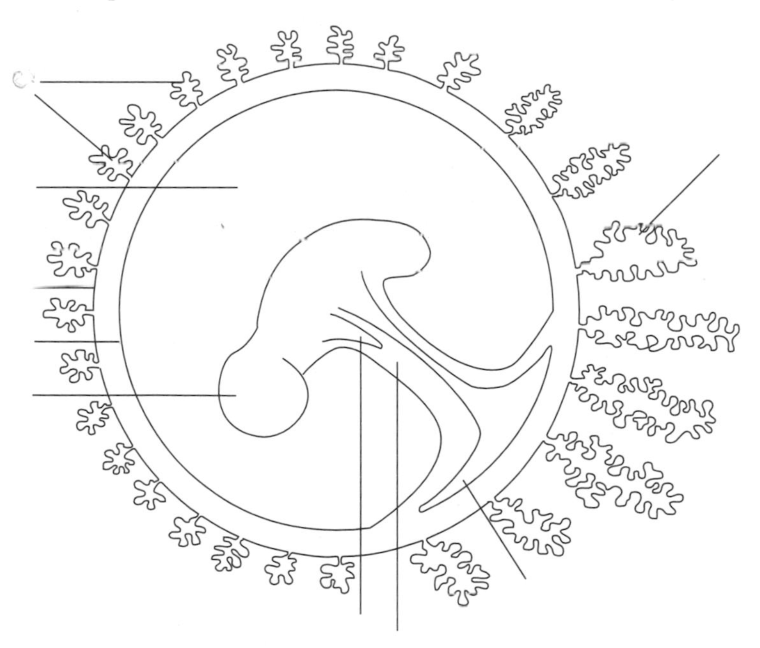

3 List the differences between insect-pollinated and wind-pollinated flowers.

EXAMINATION QUESTIONS

Question 1

Read through the following account of the hormonal control of the human menstrual cycle and then write on the dotted lines the most appropriate word or words to complete the account.

The release of .... from the anterior pituitary gland induces the development of primary follicles. Another hormone from the anterior pituitary gland stimulates the thecal cells to produce ...., which controls the repair of the .... after menstruation. At ovulation, a .... is released from the mature follicle. The remaining follicular cells form the .... which begins to secrete ...., inhibiting the release of the hormones from the anterior pituitary gland.

Total 6 marks

[London]

Question 2

In the process of sperm formation in a mammalian testis, cells divide by mitosis and by meiosis.

(a) Explain the importance of mitosis in the process of sperm formation. [2 marks]

(b) The diagram shows a mature mammalian sperm cell.

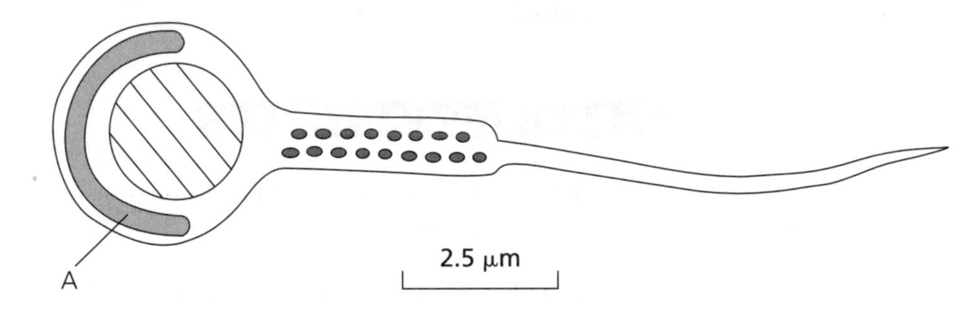

Describe the part played by structure A in the processes leading to fertilisation. [2 marks]

(c) Explain **one** advantage of internal fertilisation to a terrestrial mammal. [2 marks]

Total 6 marks

[AEB]

Question 3

The diagram below summarises the process of oogenesis in humans.

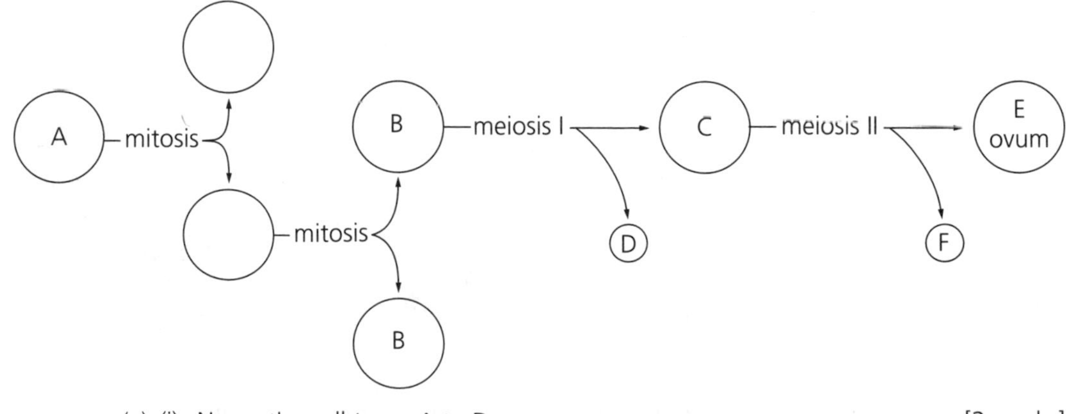

(a) (i) Name the cell types A to D. [2 marks]

(ii) State when and where cells of type B are produced. [2 marks]

(b) Compare the number of chromosomes in the following pairs of cells. A and C, E and F [2 marks]

(c) State four differences between spermatogenesis and oogenesis in humans. [4 marks]

Total 10 marks

[UCLES]

Question 4

The diagram below shows a method of grafting.

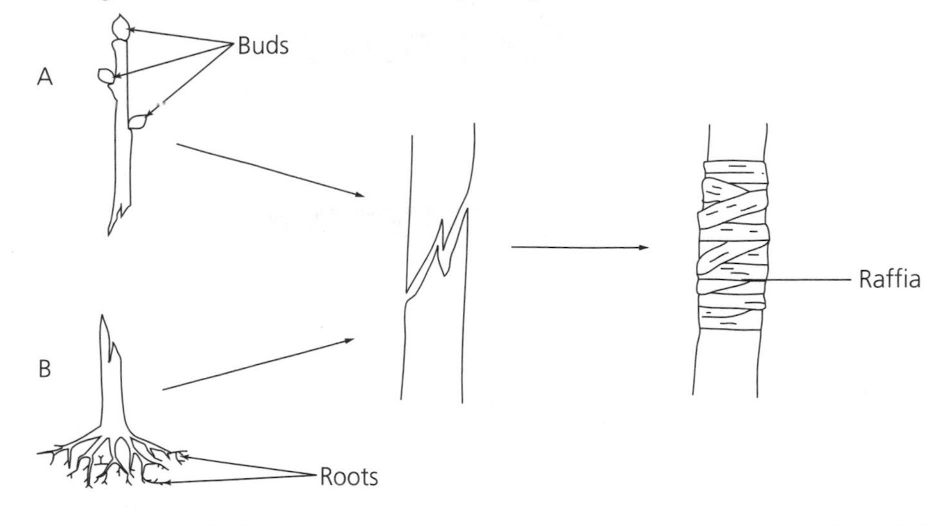

(a) Name the parts labelled A and B. [2 marks]

(b) Give two reasons for the shape of the cuts made to A and B. [2 marks]

(c) Explain why grafting is used to propagate fruit trees such as apple. [2 marks]

Total 6 marks

[London]

Question 5

The graph shows changes in the mean diameter of follicles and corpora lutea in the ovaries of a pig over a period of 50 days.

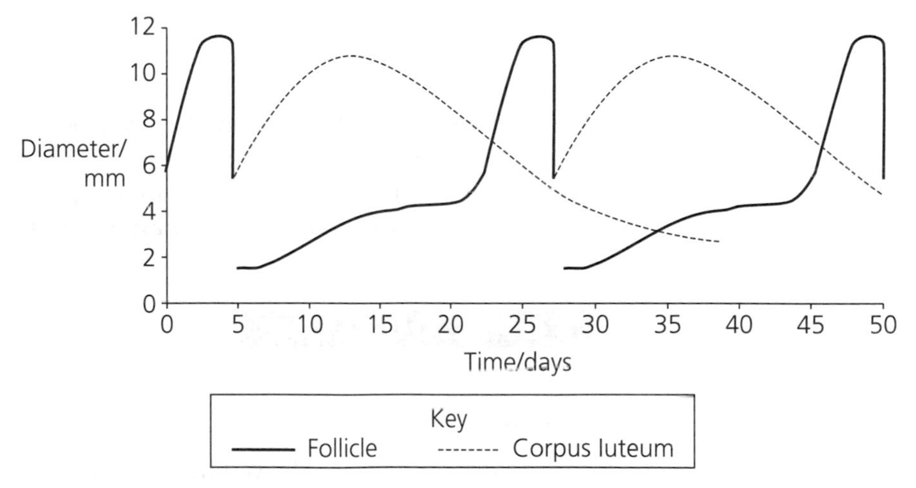

(a) (i) Explain the changes in follicle size which took place between day 5 and day 27. [2 marks]

(ii) Describe the part played by hormones in producing these changes. [3 marks]

(b) Describe two pieces of evidence which suggest that this animal did not become pregnant over the period of time shown on the graph. [2 marks]

(c) Mark the graph with an arrow (↓) to show one time when you would expect this animal to be in oestrus. [1 mark]

Total 8 marks

[AEB]

Answers to all these questions and to the revision activity can be found on pp. 86–9.
An extra question and Student answer can also be found there.

Question 6

(a) Explain what is meant by the term cross pollination. [2 marks]

(b) A plant breeder wanted to produce hybrids of two varieties, A and B, of a flower species. Outline the procedure needed to obtain the hybrid seeds. [4 marks]

Total 6 marks

[London]

7 Support, locomotion and transport

REVISION TIPS

This topic is a very large one and covers several important areas of the syllabus. You already have a sound understanding of **metabolic processes** such as respiration and photosynthesis, and of the nature of **plant and animal cells**.

The understanding of the **transport** of molecules into and out of cells requires a knowledge of the structure of **membranes**, so revise this topic before attempting to learn about diffusion and active transport. The amount of detail you need should be determined by reference to your syllabus. Some syllabuses do require you to know about **water relations** of plant cells in detail and you should always use the correct **water potential** terminology in your answers. Those who do not will not be awarded marks.

Syllabuses vary in the detail required on **locomotion**, so check thoroughly to see how much you need to know and what examples are relevant.

The areas covered in this topic are interrelated, in that support and transport in flowering plants are linked, and also related to other major topic areas in the syllabus. In the practice questions, there are several examples where more than one topic has been tested within a question.

As with other topics, the types of questions set range from very straightforward recall of knowledge to those where you are required to handle data and situations that might be unfamiliar. A good understanding of the basic concepts is necessary. Do not forget to revise the relevant practical work and be able to recognize diagrams and photographs of structures such as **blood cells** and **blood vessels**, and **transport tissues** in plants.

TOPIC OUTLINE

Support

Support in plants is achieved by the following tissues:

- **Parenchyma** which consists of living cells with thin walls. When fully turgid, these cells push against each other providing mechanical support in leaves, herbaceous stems and roots.
- **Collenchyma** which consists of elongated living cells, possessing extra cellulose thickening; often present in the outer cortex of herbaceous stems and the midribs of leaves, providing flexible support.
- **Sclerenchyma** which consists of non-living, elongated fibres with thick lignified walls. Cells have tapered ends, which interlock forming a strong tissue; found in xylem and phloem tissue, in the outer cortex of herbaceous stems and as bundle caps or sheaths round the vascular tissue in herbaceous stems.
- **Xylem** consists of vessels, tracheids, xylem fibres and xylem parenchyma. **Vessels** and **tracheids** have lignified walls, which contribute to support, but their main function is transport. **Xylem tissue** provides support in roots (central core of tissue resists pulling strains, helping anchorage), stems (part of the peripheral vascular bundles, resists bending strains) and leaves (petiole, midribs and veins).

In woody plants, secondary thickening results in an increase in the amount of xylem in the stems and the roots.

Skeletons give support to animals and three main types of skeleton are recognised.

1 **Hydrostatic** skeletons (e.g. earthworm), where the fluid-filled body cavity is surrounded by the muscles of the body wall. The fluid exerts a pressure on the body wall and the muscles of the body wall contract against the fluid, maintaining shape and enabling locomotion.
2 **Exoskeletons**, which are characteristic of the arthropods (e.g. insects). Chitin is secreted by the epidermal cells forming a light, tough covering, strengthened by proteins or by calcium salts. They possess joints allowing movement, have muscles attached inside, and form good protection but do not allow growth, so have to be shed periodically (ecdysis).
3 **Endoskeletons** (e.g. vertebrates), are typically composed of bone or cartilage and located within the organism and internal to the muscles. Joints allow movement, with bones held together by ligaments; movement is achieved by contraction and relaxation of pairs of antagonistic muscles attached to the bones by tendons.

The mammalian skeleton is divided into:

- the **axial** skeleton consisting of the skull and vertebral column
- the **appendicular** skeleton consisting of the limbs and limb girdles.

Joints occur where two or more bones meet. Three major types of joints are recognised:

1 **immovable** joints in the skull, sternum and pelvis
2 **partially movable** joints in the wrist, ankle and between the vertebrae
3 **freely movable**, or **synovial**, joints at elbows, knees and fingers (**hinge**) and shoulder and hip (**ball and socket**).

Locomotion

Movement of living organisms from one place to another is termed **locomotion**. It is brought about in a number of ways.

- **Amoeboid movement** is characteristic of protoctistans such as *Amoeba* and involves the formation of **pseudopodia**.
- Locomotion brought about by **cilia** and **flagella** is also found in small organisms such as *Paramecium* (cilia) and *Euglena* (flagella) that live in water. Such movement is also found inside multicellular organisms, where it might be used to move fluids through ducts.
- **Muscular movement** is common in multicellular animals.

Locomotion in the vertebrates is brought about by muscle contraction. **Muscles** are made up of elongated cells called muscle fibres, which can relax and contract. There are three types of muscle tissue found in mammals.

1 **Skeletal** muscle (striated, striped, voluntary), which is attached to bone by tendons; contracts quickly, tires easily; concerned with locomotion.
2 **Smooth** muscle (unstriated, unstriped, involuntary, plain), which is found in the body organs; contracts slowly, does not tire easily; concerned with the movement of materials within the body, e.g. gut.
3 **Cardiac** muscle found only in the heart.

A **skeletal muscle** has an **origin**, its **attachment** to the non-movable part of the skeleton, and an **insertion**, where it is attached to a movable part. At least two muscles, or sets of muscles, are required to move the position of a bone. These are known as **antagonistic muscles**.

A **striated muscle** is made up of **muscle fibres** each containing many myofibrils. Each muscle fibre is surrounded by a **sarcolemma** and large numbers of **mitochondria** occur between the muscle fibres. **Myofibrils** are divided into sarcomeres by cross-partitions, **the Z lines**, and within each sarcomere are two types of **protein fibres**:

1 thin strands of **actin** which project into the sarcomere from the Z lines
2 thicker **myosin** fibres.

When contraction occurs, each sarcomere shortens. The actin strands are pulled towards the centre of the sarcomere due to a ratchet mechanism achieved by the formation of cross-bridges with the myosin, the energy needed coming from ATP. Two other proteins are involved:

- **tropomyosin** switches the contractile mechanism on or off by freeing or blocking calcium-binding sites on the actin filaments;
- **troponin**, consisting of three sub-units, binds to tropomyosin, provides calcium-binding sites and can inhibit the interaction of actin and myosin if calcium ions are not present.

The presence of calcium ions, released when a muscle is stimulated by a nerve impulse, reverses the inhibitory effect of troponin and causes tropomyosin to move to a new position on the actin molecule, allowing cross-bridge formation to occur.

The contraction of muscles is controlled by **nerve fibres** which innervate the muscle fibres. Nerve muscle junctions are similar to synapses between nerve fibres and use **neurotransmitters** which depolarise the membrane of the muscle fibre to stimulate its contraction.

Transport

Before considering the way in which transport of materials occurs in plants and animals, it is essential to have an understanding of the ways in which molecules and ions are able to move through the cell surface membrane. Materials enter and leave cells by:

- diffusion
- facilitated diffusion
- osmosis
- active transport
- endocytosis and exocytosis.

Diffusion is the movement of molecules or ions from a region where they are in high concentration to a region where they are in lower concentration. There will be a net movement down the concentration gradient until there is a uniform distribution or equilibrium is reached. The process is passive as it does not require metabolic energy. The **rate of diffusion** depends on

- the **concentration gradient**: the steeper the gradient, the greater the rate;
- the **size of the ions or molecules**: the smaller they are, the greater the rate;
- the **distance** over which diffusion occurs: the shorter the distance the greater the rate.

Diffusion in living organisms involves the passage of molecules and ions across the cell surface membrane and internal membranes within cells, so these membranes must be permeable to the diffusing substances. All cell membranes are permeable to oxygen, carbon dioxide and water.

Diffusion accounts for:

- the movement of gases in respiration and photosynthesis, and
- the distribution of food materials.

Facilitated diffusion is a modified form of diffusion in which some **polar molecules** and **ions** are transported across cell membranes by **protein carriers**. An example of such transport is shown by the movement of glucose molecules into red blood cells. Again, no energy expenditure is involved and the diffusion occurs down a concentration gradient.

Osmosis is a special case of diffusion involving the passage of solvent molecules from a region of high concentration to a region of lower concentration through a partially, or selectively, permeable membrane. In living organisms, the solvent is water and the membranes are the cell surface membrane and internal cell membranes. Water movement is linked to the movement and concentration of solutes on either side of the membrane.

The term **water potential** is used by biologists to describe the tendency of water molecules to move from high to low concentrations, so water will diffuse from a region of high water potential to a region of lower water potential. In situations where there is a high concentration of water molecules, the water molecules have a greater potential energy, and in situations where there is a lower concentration of water molecules, their potential energy is less. The water potential of water at atmospheric pressure is given a value of **zero**, so all **solutions** have **lower** potentials than pure water and hence **negative** values.

Active transport involves the movement of molecules across a membrane up a concentration gradient and of ions up their electrochemical gradients. Most active transport systems involve **sodium-potassium pumps**, which are driven by metabolic energy derived from **ATP**. Active transport allows the uptake of ions and molecules needed for metabolism and for the removal of waste products.

Endocytosis and **exocytosis** are involved with the bulk transport of materials through membranes. Both processes depend on the fluidity of the cell membrane: endocytosis involving **uptake of materials** and exocytosis the **removal of materials** from cells. Invagination of the cell membrane occurs in endocytosis, an example of which is observed in the uptake of food by *Amoeba*, a process known as **phagocytosis**. Exocytosis is observed in **secretory cells**, where enzymes are formed within the endoplasmic reticulum and modified in the Golgi apparatus before being released when the vesicles fuse with the cell membrane.

In unicellular organisms and those multicellular organisms with a large surface area to volume ratio, transport by diffusion appears to be efficient, but in bulkier animals and plants a specialised transport system is necessary.

In many **animals**, transport systems involving **blood** are present. The blood system usually consists of **tubular vessels** through which blood is circulated by a **pumping device**. There are two types of blood circulatory systems:

1. **open** – in which the blood is pumped by the heart into a series of blood spaces or haemocoels, e.g. insects;
2. **closed** – in which the blood is confined to blood vessels, e.g. earthworms.

In **vertebrates** there are two types of closed circulation systems with muscular hearts.

1. **Single circulation systems**, present in fish, where blood is pumped to the gills to be oxygenated, from where it passes to the rest of the body before returning to the heart.
2. **Double circulation systems**, evident in mammals, where blood is pumped from the heart to the lungs to be oxygenated, then passes back to the heart to be pumped around the body in a completely separate circulation.

In **vertebrates**, blood is made up of **cells** in **plasma**. There are three main types of blood cells:

1. **Erythrocytes** – red blood corpuscles – contain haemoglobin and are responsible for the transport of oxygen from the lungs to the respiring cells.
2. **Leucocytes** – white blood corpuscles – of which there are several types: **neutrophils**, **basophils** and **eosinophils** are all **granulocytes**; **monocytes** and **lymphocytes** are **agranulocytes**.
3. **Thrombocytes** – platelets – involved in the blood-clotting mechanism.

Blood is pumped by the heart into **arteries**, which carry blood to the tissues, where they split up into **arterioles**. The blood passes from the arterioles into the **capillaries**, a vast network of tiny vessels which permeate the tissues and organs. Exchange of materials occurs and the blood passes into **venules**, which unite to form **veins** carrying the blood back to the heart.

Arteries and veins have the same basic three-layered structure, but the proportions of the different layers varies. Both have:

- an **endothelium** as the innermost layer, providing a smooth lining one cell thick
- a middle layer composed of **elastic fibres** and **smooth muscle**, which is much thicker in the arteries than the veins
- an outer layer of **collagen fibres** which resist overstretching.

The capillaries have walls which are one cell thick. Veins differ from arteries in that they possess **semilunar valves** which prevent the backflow of blood away from the heart.

The heart in mammals is **four-chambered**, consisting of a **right** and **left atrium** and a **right** and **left ventricle**. **Deoxygenated blood** enters the right atrium from the **venae cavae**. It passes through the **tricuspid valve** into the right ventricle from where it is pumped to the **lungs** via the **pulmonary arteries**. When the ventricle muscle contracts, the tricuspid valve closes preventing the backflow of blood into the atrium, and the semilunar valves in the walls of the pulmonary arteries are forced open. Blood returning from the lungs via the **pulmonary veins** enters the left atrium, passes through the bicuspid valve into the left ventricle from where it is pumped to the rest of the body by contraction of the left ventricle. Reference should be made to diagrams of the heart and the general circulation.

The heart is composed of **cardiac muscle**, which is **myogenic**. Within the right atrium is the **sino-atrial node**, or **pacemaker**, which initiates the heartbeat and from which a wave of stimulation spreads over the atria. When this reaches the **atrio-ventricular node**, the excitation is passed along the **bundle of His** and spreads through the **Purkinje tissue** in the walls of the ventricles causing them to contract. The **rate** at which the heart beats is modified by the **nervous system**: stimulation of the **vagus nerve** will **slow down** the heartbeat, stimulation of the **sympathetic nervous system** will **accelerate** it.

Transport in **flowering plants** involves the vascular tissues, which are made up of:

- **xylem**, which transports water and mineral ions from the roots to the leaves
- **phloem**, which transports the soluble products of photosynthesis from the leaves to all other parts of the plant.

In the xylem, the **vessels** and **tracheids** are the main conducting cells. They have **lignified walls** and a hollow **lumen**. The **lignin** provides strength and prevents the collapse of the cells under pressure. The **vessels** are formed from long chains of vessel segments joined end to end. The end walls break down leaving a long tube ideally suited to the transport of water. Due to transpiration and photosynthesis, there is water loss from the aerial parts of the plant and this water is replaced from the xylem. The adhesive forces which exist between the water molecules and the walls of the xylem vessels, together with the cohesive forces attracting the water molecules to each other combine to maintain the columns of water in the xylem.

Water enters the plant through the **root hairs**, travels across the **cortex** and into the **xylem**. The passage across the cortex can be through:

- the **cellulose cell walls**, known as the **apoplast pathway**, depending on mass flow and the cohesion of the water molecules
- the **cytoplasm** and **plasmodesmata** in the **symplast pathway**
- the **vacuolar pathway**, from vacuole to vacuole down a water potential gradient.

It travels in the xylem up through the stem to the leaves, where most of it evaporates from the internal leaf surfaces and passes out as water vapour into the atmosphere in the process of **transpiration**. Transpiration is the inevitable consequence of the opening of the stomata for gas exchange.

The **rate of transpiration** is dependent on external factors such as temperature, humidity and air movements. It can be demonstrated using a **potometer**.

The main conducting cells in **phloem** are **sieve tubes**, which are formed from sieve elements placed end to end. The end walls remain intact, but become perforated by pores, which allow substances to pass from cell to cell. Most of the organelles, including the nucleus, degenerate, leaving a few fragments of endoplasmic reticulum, but the central part of each cell contains **protein filaments**, which are continuous with similar filaments in other sieve tube elements. Each sieve tube element is associated with a companion cell, containing dense cytoplasm, large nucleus and many mitochondria. Sugars and amino acids, formed during photosynthesis, enter the sieve tubes by an active process involving transfer cells.

Several hypotheses have been put forward to account for the movement of substances in the phloem. The best documented of these is the **mass flow hypothesis**, but others include **electro-osmosis**, **surface spreading** and **cytoplasmic streaming**.

REVISION ACTIVITY

The diagram below represents the human circulatory system.

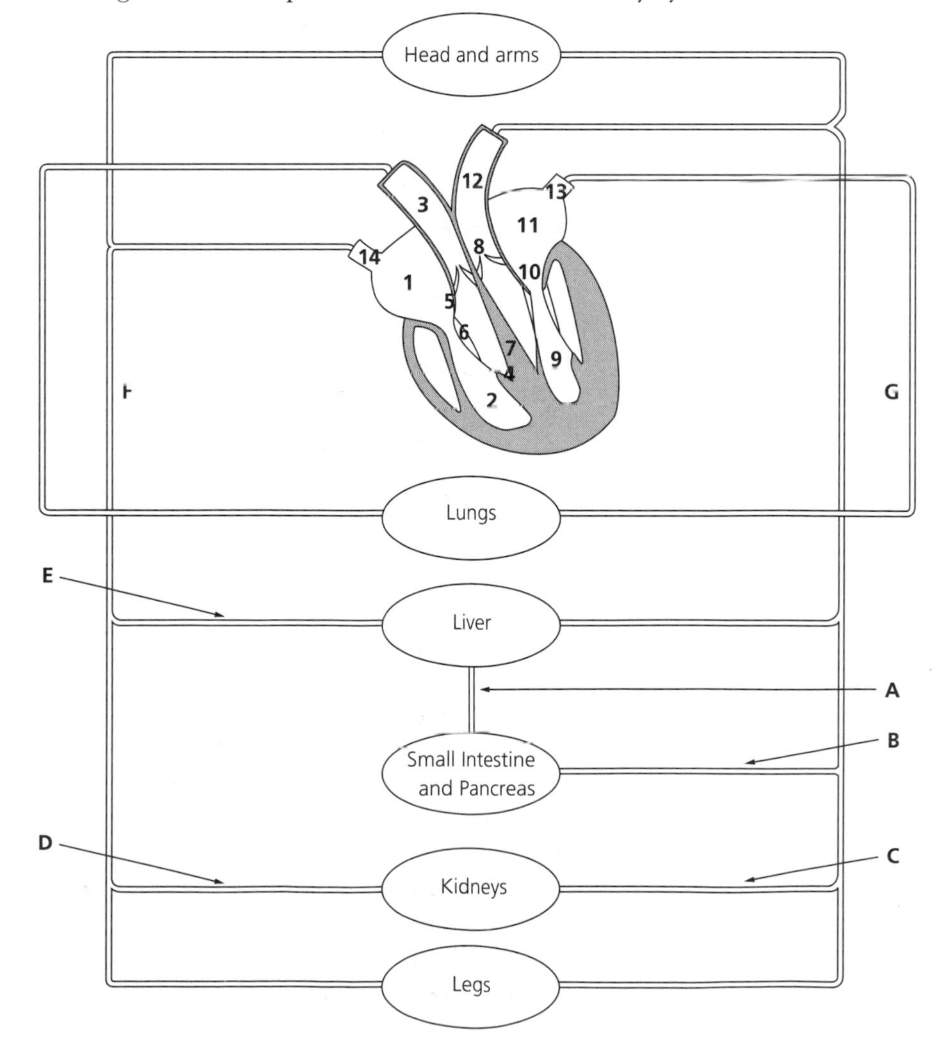

(a) Identify the structures labelled 1 to 14 in the area of the heart.
(b) Give the differences in the composition of the blood in
A and B after a meal
C and D
A and E
F and G
Try to give reasons for these differences.

This revision activity does cover more than the content of this topic, but you will often find questions on examination papers which cover more than one syllabus area, i.e. that have a synoptic element.

EXAMINATION QUESTIONS

Question 1

The table below refers to the structure and functions of xylem vessels and phloem sieve tubes in plants.
If the statement is correct, place a tick (✓) in the appropriate box and if the statement is incorrect, place a cross (✗) in the appropriate box.

Statement	*Xylem vessels*	*Phloem sieve tubes*
Possess living contents		
Provide support		
Composed of cells fused together end to end		
Walls contain lignin		

Total 4 marks
[London]

The following question tests material not in this topic.

Question 2

The diagram below shows the main muscles in a human leg.

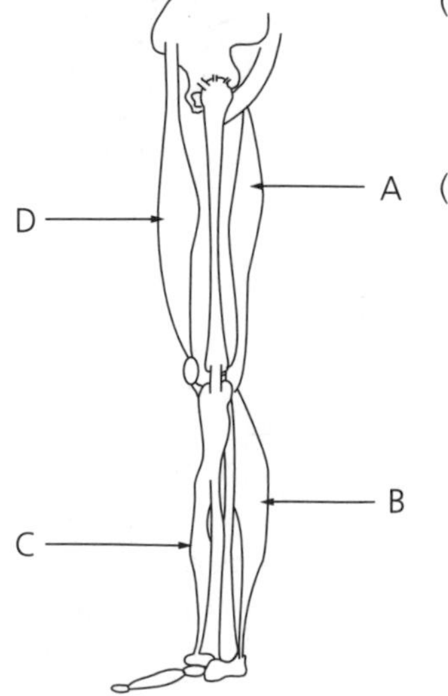

(a) Which of muscles A to D on the diagram
(i) must contract to raise the heel from the ground?
(ii) is antagonistic to this muscle? [2 marks]

(b) While walking barefoot on the beach, a person stands on a sharp stone.
(i) Briefly describe the pathway of the reflex arc involved in responding to this stimulus.

(You are not required to give details of the propagation of nerve impulses.)

[3 marks]

(ii) Suggest one advantage of reflexes such as this one. [1 mark]

Total 6 marks
[NEAB]

Question 3

A respiring cell gains oxygen by the process of simple diffusion; it gains most of its glucose by facilitated diffusion.

(a) Give
  (i) one similarity between simple diffusion and facilitated diffusion [1 mark]
  (ii) one difference between simple diffusion and facilitated diffusion [1 mark]

(b) The rate of diffusion through a membrane is proportional to:

$$\frac{\text{surface area} \times \text{difference in concentration}}{\text{thickness of membrane}}$$

Predict whether the value of each of the three variables will be high or low when the rate of diffusion through the membrane is at a maximum.
  (i) surface area
  (ii) difference in concentration
  (iii) thickness of membrane [1 mark]

(c) Explain the following observations.
  (i) The rate of diffusion of chloride ions from carrot tissue increases with temperature. [1 mark]
  (ii) Loss of sodium ions from nerve cells stops if the tissue is treated with the respiratory poison, cyanide. [1 mark]

Total 5 marks

[AEB]

Question 4

The bar chart shows the relative thickness of parts of the walls of two blood vessels, A and B. One of these blood vessels was an artery, the other was a vein.

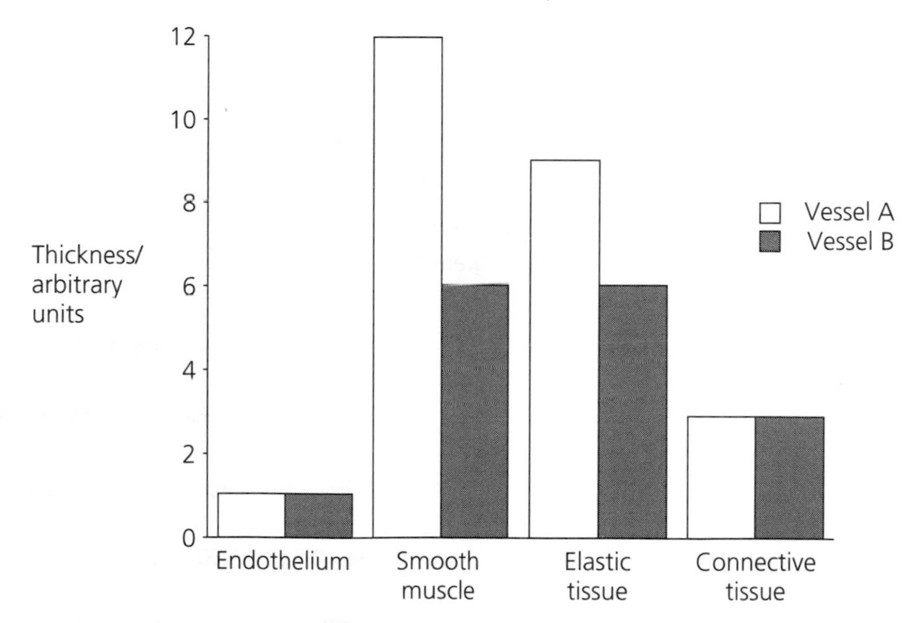

(a) Explain why the thickness of the endothelium is the same for both blood vessels. [1 mark]

(b) Which blood vessel is the artery? Explain the reason for your answer. [2 marks]

(c) Explain how the structure of veins ensures the flow of blood in one direction only. [2 marks]

Total 5 marks

[NEAB]

Question 5

The diagram shows the spread of electrical activity over the surface of a human heart. The figures are times in seconds.

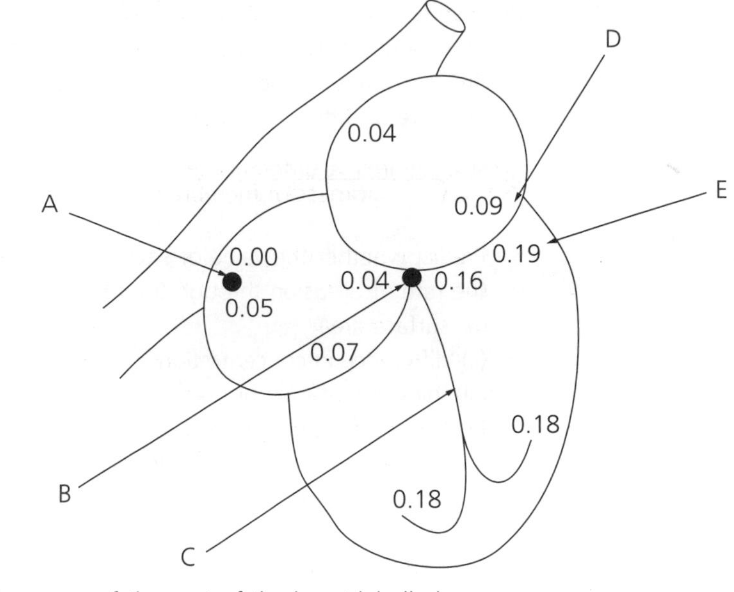

(a) Give the name of the part of the heart labelled
(i) A (ii) C [2 marks]
(b) What is the importance of the time delay between the electrical activity arriving at and leaving the part of the heart labelled B? [2 marks]
(c) Use the information on the diagram to explain the difference in time between the electrical activity arriving at point D and its arrival at point E. [2 marks]
(d) Describe and explain the difference between the pressure of the blood leaving the left ventricle and the pressure of the blood leaving the right ventricle. [2 marks]
(e) Explain how sympathetic stimulation increases cardiac output. [3 marks]

Total 11 marks

[AEB]

Question 6

The diagram below shows a sarcomere from a myofibril of a striated muscle fibre.

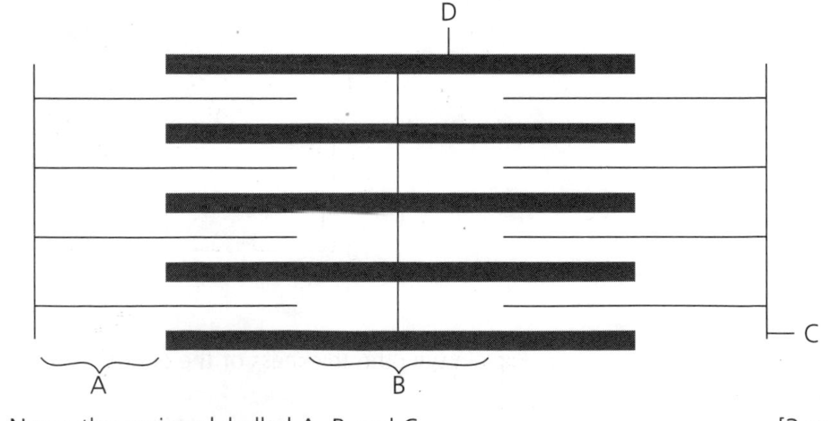

(a) (i) Name the regions labelled A, B and C. [3 marks]
(ii) Name the material which makes up part D. [1 mark]
(b) State the change in appearance of B when the muscle fibre contracts. [1 mark]

Total 5 marks

[London]

Answers to all these questions and to the revision activity can be found on pp. 89–92.
An extra question and Student answer can also be found there.

8 Coordination and homeostasis

REVISION TIPS

Coordination in animals and also homeostatic control are brought about by the interaction of the **nervous system** and the **endocrine system**. You need to be confident that you know the structure and physiology of the nervous system and the general principles of hormonal control. Check your syllabus to see which particular **hormones** you need to know in detail. Make sure that you understand the phenomenon of **negative feedback** and be able to describe and explain at least one example in detail. Again, check your syllabus as a particular example may be specified.

All the syllabuses include the five major types of plant growth substances. These are concerned with the **growth**, **development** and **senescence** processes in plants and so are responsible for **chemical coordination**. In particular, be sure that you understand the **synergistic** and **antagonistic** interactions between them. As well as these growth substances, plants also contain a photoreceptor pigment, **phytochrome**. Be sure that you are familiar with the effects that this has on the physiology of plants and in particular with the **photoperiodic effects** and the control of **flowering**.

TOPIC OUTLINE

Nervous systems

- The simplest nervous system, found in lower multicellular animals such as cnidarians is an undifferentiated **nerve net**.
- Higher invertebrates such as annelids, arthropods and molluscs have nerve cells aggregated into **ganglia** from which nerves arise.
- The nervous system of vertebrates consists of a **central nervous system** of brain and spinal cord and a system of **peripheral nerves.**
- The brain is divided into **fore**, **mid** and **hind** brains.
- The major part of the fore brain, the **cerebrum** is concerned with all the higher mental activities. The **thalamus** is a relay system and the **hypothalamus** is concerned with the control of basic drives and emotions.
- The hind brain has two main parts, the **medulla** and the **cerebellum**. The medulla contains the cardiac, vasomotor and respiratory centres and is the origin of much of the autonomic nervous system. The cerebellum is concerned with the coordination of body movements and with postural responses.
- The spinal cord has a central area of **grey matter** containing nerve cell bodies and outer **white matter** consisting of nerve fibres. It gives rise to the **spinal nerves** which relay information to and from the brain.
- The **peripheral** nervous system consists of **afferent** (**sensory**) nerves bringing information to the brain from the sense organs and **efferent** (**motor**) nerves taking impulses to the effector organs.
- The **autonomic** nervous system consists of two sets of nerves working antagonistically to regulate the function of the internal organs. It is central to the processes of **homeostasis**. The **sympathetic** system acts to increase the body's ability to be active. The **parasympathetic** system is antagonistic

to the sympathetic system. It reduces blood flow and respiratory rate and increases activity in the gut.

- Nerve impulses pass along the nerve fibres by **ionic exchange** through the cell membrane of the fibres. At rest there is a potential of −60 mV across the membrane. Stimuli bring about an **action potential** by the passage of sodium ions into the fibre. This **depolarisation** passes along the fibre.
- Axons with a **myelin sheath** pass impulses more rapidly.
- Most junctions between nerve fibres are by **chemical synapses**. The impulse passes across the synapse by the diffusion of a **neurotransmitter**, for example **acetyl choline**.
- Sensory receptors give a continuous input to the nervous system. Four types of stimuli are received. **Photoreceptors** receive light. **Chemoreceptors** are concerned with taste and smell. **Mechanoreceptors** receive information about sound, touch, pressure and gravity. **Thermoreceptors** deal with temperature change.

Endocrine system

- This is a system of **ductless glands** secreting **hormones** directly into the blood stream.
- Hormones are concerned with the control of body function. The control mechanisms depend upon the activity of one part of the system influencing the activity of other parts. This a **feedback** system. The endocrine system is controlled by **negative feedback** where there is a relationship between the level of the product and the releasing mechanism. This increases the stability of the internal environment, that is, **homeostasis**.
- Much of the activity of the endocrine system is controlled by hormones produced by the **pituitary** gland under the influence of the hypothalamus. For example, adrenocorticotrophic hormone (**ACTH**) stimulates the adrenal cortex, and thyroid stimulating hormone (**TSH**) stimulates the thyroid.
- Blood glucose level is controlled by two antagonistic hormones, **insulin** and **glucagon** produced by the **islets of Langerhans** in the **pancreas**.

Homeostasis

- This is the maintenance of the stability of the internal environment within the body giving an organism some independence from the external environment. Homeostasis in mammals is achieved under the influence of the **hypothalamus** which monitors pH, osmotic pressure and temperature. It brings about regulation either by direct effect on the autonomic nervous system or via hormones from the pituitary gland.
- The **kidney** removes nitrogenous waste from the blood and maintains the fluid composition of the body by regulating both water and the ionic content.
- The **liver** controls metabolic levels in the body and is involved in **thermogenesis**.

Chemical coordination in plants

- There are five major types of plant growth substances which are essential for **cell division**, **cell elongation** and **cell differentiation**.
- **Auxins** enable cellulose microfibrils to slide past each other so that the cell wall can stretch more easily when water is absorbed by osmosis. They are involved in the **phototropic** responses of shoots and the **geotropic** responses of shoots and roots.

- **Gibberellins** also affect cell elongation and are more active in young plant organs. They are also involved in breaking **dormancy** in bulbs and seeds by stimulating the activation of enzymes involved in mobilising food reserves.
- **Cytokinins** are involved with cell division. They work **synergistically** with auxins and gibberellins
- **Abscisic acid** is a growth inhibitor. It is **antagonistic** to the action of all the other growth substances, promoting dormancy in buds and seeds, and it is involved in fruit and leaf fall.
- **Ethene** is produced by most plant organs and it influences fruit ripening by promoting a rapid increase in respiration rate.
- As well as the growth substances, the blue-green pigment, **phytochrome** is involved in plant responses. It occurs in very small quantities and occurs in two forms. One form absorbs red light with an absorption peak at 665 nm. This is referrred to as P_R or P_{665}. The other form absorbs far red light with an absorption peak at 725 nm and is referred to as P_{FR} or P_{725}. When P_R absorbs red light it is converted to P_{FR} and vice versa. P_{FR} tends to accumulate in daylight and P_R at night. The phytochrome system is important for many aspects of plant growth such as germination in some seeds (e.g. lettuce), stem elongation, leaf expansion, growth of lateral roots and flowering.
- **Photoperiodism** is the effect of the relative lengths of periods of light and darkness on the activities of plants. It has an important effect on flowering.
- In **day neutral plants** flowering is unaffected by day length, e.g. tomato and cucumber.
- In **long day plants**, flowering is induced by exposure to dark periods shorter than a critical length, e.g. cabbage and petunia.
- In **short day plants** flowering is induced by exposure to dark periods longer than a critical length, e.g. chrysanthemums and poinsettias.
- Flowering in short day plants is inhibited by exposure to **red light** and exposure to **far red light** will bring about flowering. These plants only flower if levels of P_{FR} are low enough. Flowering in long day plants is triggered by high levels of P_{FR}. The photoperiodic stimulus is perceived by the leaves. The stimulus is transmitted to the buds which then form flowers. It is suggested that the phytochrome causes the production of a hormone, **florigen**.

REVISION ACTIVITY

1 List the hormones produced by the following endocrine glands and for each hormone give its roles within the mammalian body.
(i) anterior pituitary (ii) thyroid gland
(iii) islets of Langerhans (iv) adrenal medulla

2 Draw a fully labelled diagram to show the structure of the spinal cord and a spinal reflex arc.

3 Describe three experiments that demonstrate the phototropic effect of unidirectional light on oat coleoptiles and the role of auxins in this effect.

EXAMINATION QUESTIONS

Question 1

The diagram summarises the homeostatic control of blood glucose levels by insulin in mammals.

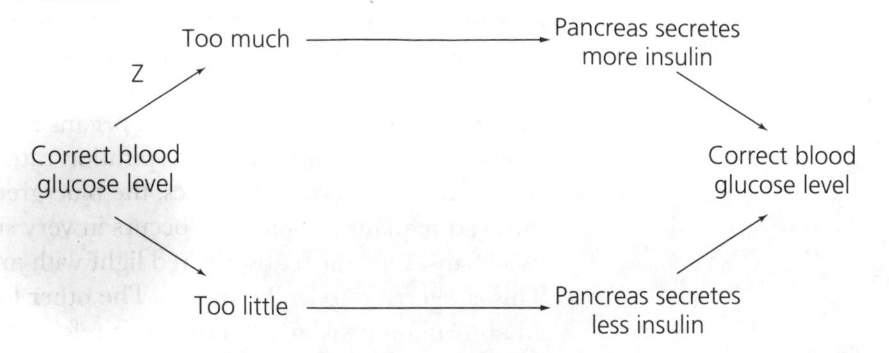

(a) (i) Name the type of homeostatic mechanism illustrated above. [1 mark]
(ii) Suggest one reason for the sudden change in blood glucose level in the region labelled Z. [1 mark]
(iii) The hormone insulin does not enter a cell. Suggest how it may bring about a change in glucose metabolism in a cell. [1 mark]

(b) Germinating barley seeds produce a hormone which increases glucose levels in the embryo plant.
(i) Describe fully how this increase in glucose levels is achieved in the embryo plant. [2 marks]
(ii) Explain why the term homeostasis is not applied to this process. [1 mark]

Total 6 marks

[WJEC]

Question 2

The graph shows changes in permeability of an axon membrane to sodium and potassium ions during an action potential in a neurone.

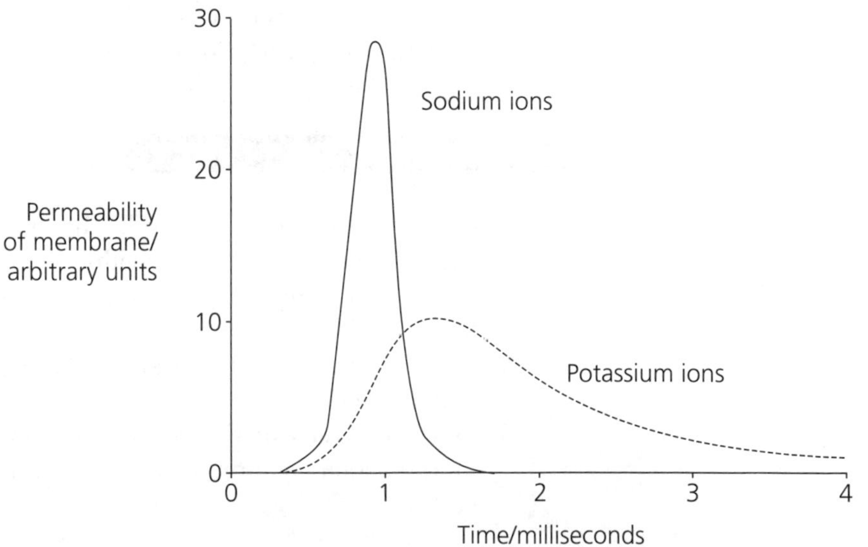

(a) Use information in the graph to explain why, at the start of an action potential, the potential difference across the membrane rapidly changes from negative to positive. [2 marks]

(b) Suggest why, during a period of intense nervous activity, the metabolic rate of a nerve cell increases. [2 marks]

(c) Predict the effect on an action potential of lowering the external concentration of sodium ions. Explain your answer. [2 marks]

Total 6 marks

[AEB]

Question 3

The diagram below shows the simplified structure of a kidney tubule (nephron).

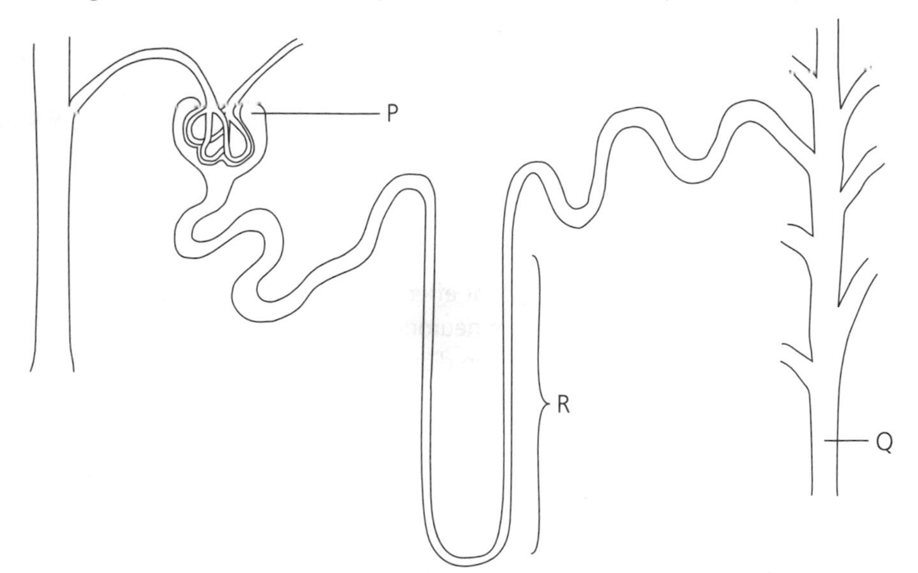

(a) In the table below, columns 1 and 2 show the quantities of water, glucose and urea passing through P and Q in a 24-hour period.
Columns 3 and 4 show the quantities and percentages reabsorbed during the same period.
Complete the table by writing the correct figures in the boxes labelled (i) to (iv).

Substance	***Quantity passing through P***	***Quantity passing through Q***	***Quantity reabsorbed***	***Percentage reabsorbed***
Water	180 dm^3	1.5 dm^3	178.5 dm^3	(i)
Glucose	180 g	(ii)	180 g	100
Urea	53 g	25 g	(iii)	(iv)

[4 marks]

(b) Describe how R is involved in adjusting the concentration of the filtrate as it passes through the medulla of the kidney. [3 marks]

Total 7 marks

[London]

Question 4

The diagram below shows part of a sensory neurone and a motor neurone in a simple reflex arc. The potential differences across the axon membranes at the nodes of Ranvier are shown.

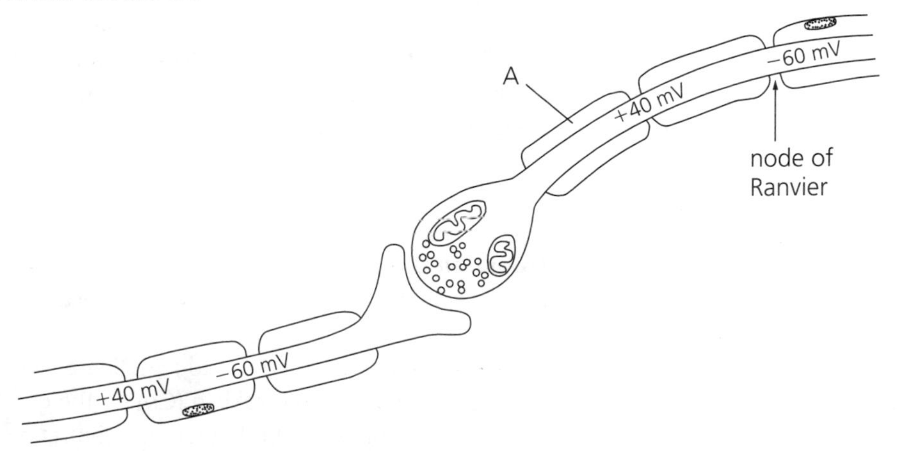

(a) On the diagram, label each of the following. In each case, explain how you made your decision.

(i) Where you would find receptors for a transmitter substance. [2 marks]
(ii) The axon of the motor neurone. [2 marks]
(iii) Where an action potential is occurring. [2 marks]

(b) State the name of, or write the chemical symbol for, an ion which
(i) diffuses into the presynaptic neurone when an action potential arrives, and causes the vesicles to fuse with the presynaptic membrane [1 mark]
(ii) is in higher concentration outside a resting neurone than inside it, and floods into the neurone when an action potential is generated [1 mark]

(c) (i) Name part A. [1 mark]
(ii) What is part A made of? [2 marks]
(iii) What effects does part A have on the transmission of action potentials along the neurone? [2 marks]

(d) In certain diseases, the motor neurones are progressively damaged.
Suggest two ways in which a person with such a disease may be affected. [2 marks]

Total 15 marks
[UCLES]

Question 5

The brain plays an important part in controlling the temperature and solute concentration of the blood. This is summarised in the diagram.

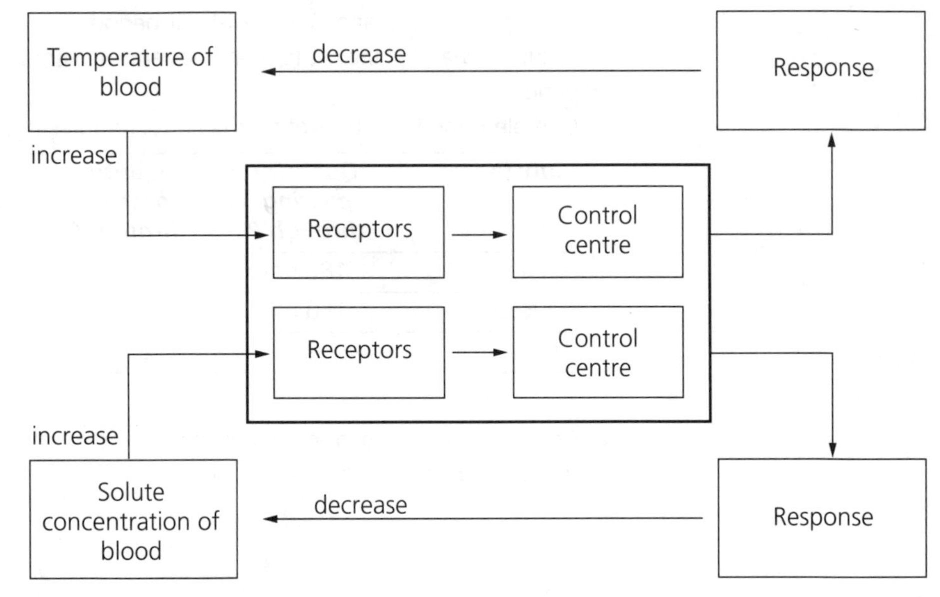

(a) Name the part of the brain which is involved in controlling the temperature and solute concentration of the blood. [1 mark]

(b) Use one of the examples in the diagram to explain the meaning of negative feedback. [2 marks]

(c) The sympathetic nervous system is involved in the regulation of blood temperature.
(i) What is the main role of the sympathetic nervous system in the body? [1 mark]
(ii) Suggest one advantage of regulating blood temperature by the nervous system rather than by hormones. [1 mark]

Total 5 marks
[NEAB]

Question 6

It is important for commercial growers of salad crops to achieve a high percentage of germination.

An experiment was carried out to investigate the effect of gibberellic acid (GA), abscisic acid (ABA), and cytokinin (CK) on the germination of lettuce seeds. Batches of seeds were immersed in different concentrations of gibberellic acid (GA) at 20 °C and the percentage germination determined.

Further batches of seeds were immersed in the same range of concentration of gibberellic acid to which abscisic acid had been added (GA + ABA) and to which both abscisic acid and cytokinin had been added (GA + ABA + CK). The percentage germination of these seeds was determined as before.

The concentration of abscisic acid used was 0.04 mmol dm^{-3}.
The concentration of cytokinin used was 0.05 mmol dm^{-3}.

The treatment and results are summarised in the table below.

Concentration of GA / mmol dm^{-3}	***Percentage germination***		
	GA only	***GA + ABA***	***GA + ABA + CK***
0	10	0	0
0.05	20	0	15
0.50	65	0	55
5.00	90	0	70

(a) Describe the effect of gibberellic acid on the percentage germination of the lettuce seeds. [3 marks]
(b) Suggest an explanation for the effect of adding abscisic acid to the gibberellic acid solutions on the percentage of the seeds germinating. [2 marks]
(c) Comment on the effect of the addition of cytokinin on the percentage germination of the seeds. [2 marks]
d) (i) State one environmental condition, other than temperature, which would need to be controlled in this experiment. [1 mark]
(ii) Suggest two further investigations which could be carried out to increase our knowledge of the effects of these plant growth substances on the germination of seeds. [2 marks]

Total 10 marks

[London]

Answers to all these questions and to the revision activity can be found on pp. 92–7.
An extra question and Student answer can also be found there.

part III
Answers and grading

1 Solutions
Molecules, cells and organelles

SOLUTION TO REVISION ACTIVITY

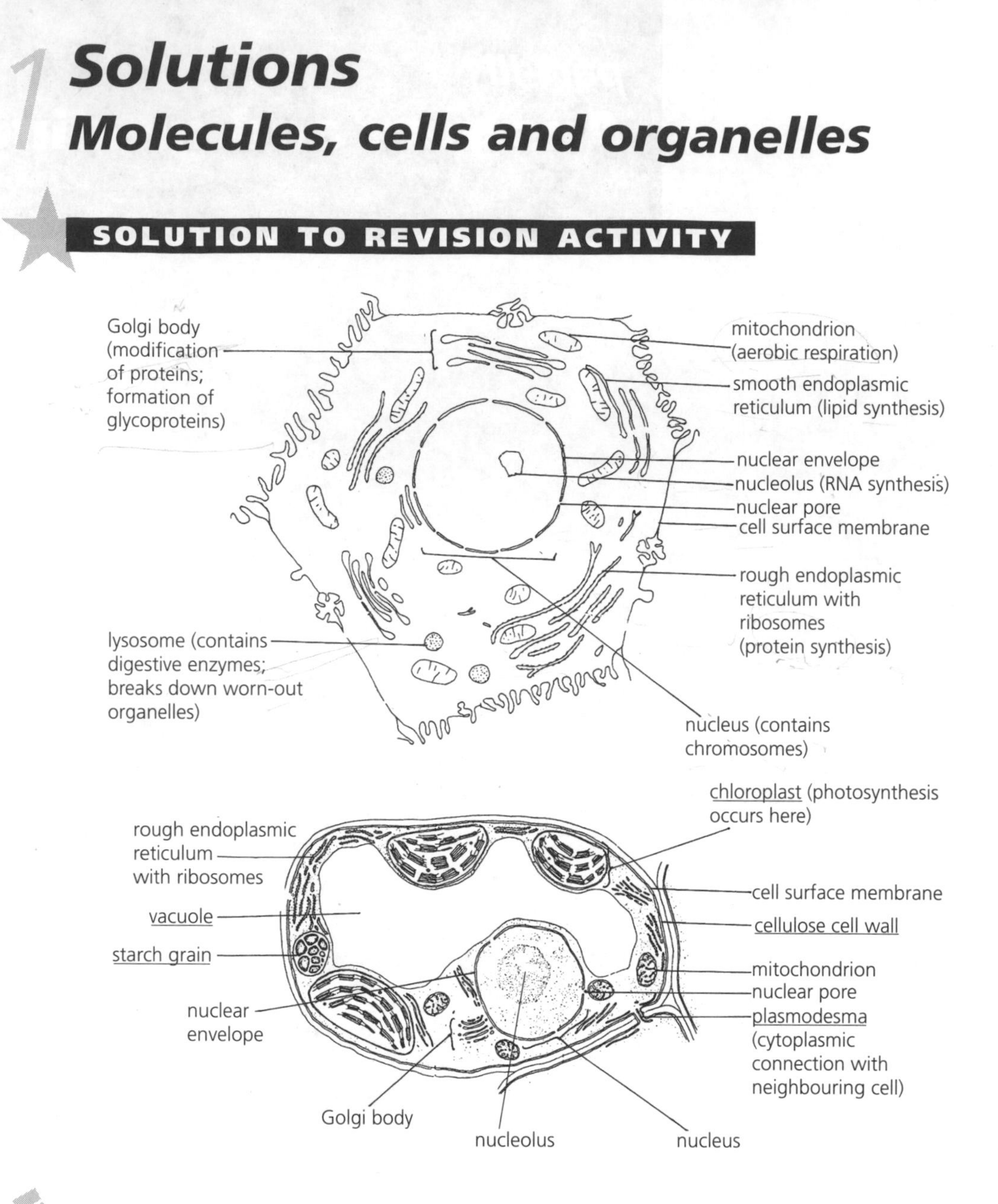

ANSWERS TO EXAMINATION QUESTIONS

Question 1

Organelle	Phospholipid	DNA	RNA
Ribosome	✗	✗	✓
Chloroplast	✓	✓	✓
Smooth endoplasmic reticulum	✓	✗	✗
Mitochondrion	✓	✓	✓

Total 4 marks

Question 2

(a) **A** deoxyribose **B** phosphate group **C** organic base (or could give named example)
D hydrogen bond [4 marks]

(b) (i) a ring on the diagram to include phosphate, deoxyribose and base from one chain [1 mark]

(ii) condensation [1 mark]

Total 6 marks

Question 3

(a) (i) **P** = amino acid **Q** = lipid; **R** = glucose (ii) nitrogen (iii) protein or polypeptide (iv) peptide (v) polysaccharide [7 marks]

(b)

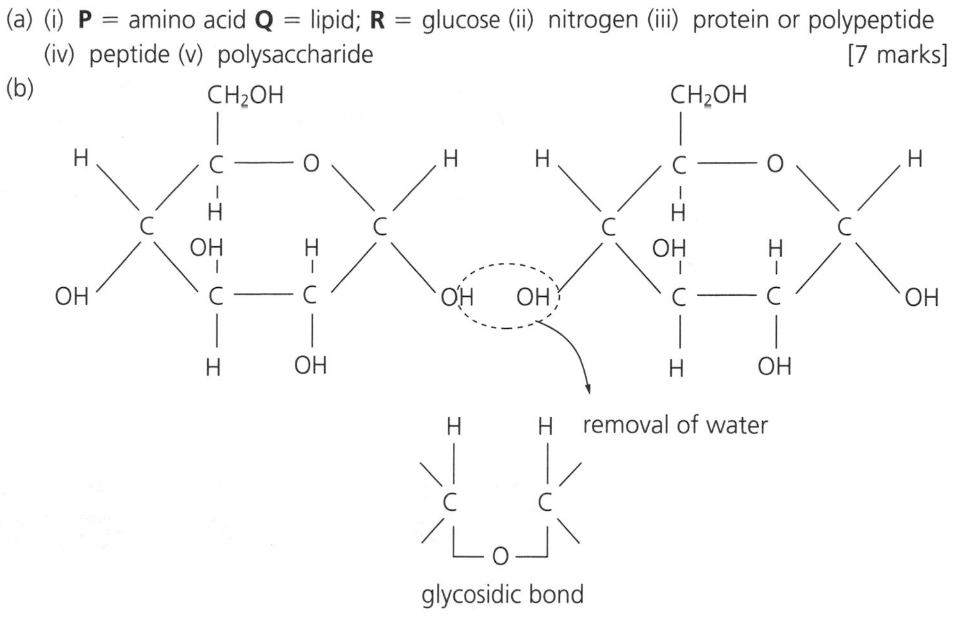

[2 marks]

(c) (i) Add potassium hydroxide until the solution clears, then add a drop of copper sulphate down the side of the tube; a blue ring should appear which disappears on shaking and the solution turns purple (Biuret test). [2 marks]

(ii) Add 5 cm^3 ethanol (absolute) and shake; add an equal volume of water and if lipid is present a cloudy white precipitate forms. [2 marks]

Note that there could be alternative answers to both (c)(i) and (c)(ii) as these are not the only tests for proteins and lipids.

Total 13 marks

Question 4

(a) Water is a polar molecule. Hydrogen bonds are formed between the oxygen atom of one water molecule and hydrogen atoms of other water molecules. It requires a large amount of heat energy to bring about a change from a liquid state to a vapour. Not so many bonds are formed between the ethanol molecules, so not so much energy is required for a change of state. [2 marks]

(b) It is important in temperature regulation. If body temperature of mammal rises above normal, sweat is released. Evaporation of the water in the sweat occurs using heat from the body, thus the mammal loses heat. [3 marks]

(c) It means that the temperature of the water will not change very quickly or very much, so providing a stable environment. It is important for the organisms to have a stable temperature for their metabolic processes. [2 marks]

(d) 1 It is a solvent for polar molecules and ionic compounds.
2 Cohesive properties; water molecules stick together so it flows through the blood vessels. [2 marks]

Total 9 marks

Question 5

(a) (i) phospholipid (ii) cellulose [2 marks]

(b) nitrogen [1 mark]

(c) 1 compact shape means that it does not take up much room.
2 It is insoluble so does not get involved with metabolic reactions or affect the osmotic balance. [2 marks]

(d) They have a three-dimensional configuration which will bind with a receptor site on the outside of a target cell. [1 mark]

Total 6 marks

Question 6

In the answer to this free prose question, reference could be made to the following:

Polysaccharides consist of monosaccharide sub-units joined by glycosidic bonds; details of formation of a glycosodic bond; α glucose in starch and glycogen; β glucose in cellulose; reference to the different types of linkage; starch consists of amylose and amylopectin; amylose unbranched chains, amylopectin branched chains; glycogen branched chains; cellulose unbranched chains; starch and glycogen as storage carbohydrates; starch in plants; glycogen in animals; both insoluble; can be broken down to glucose; yield energy; cellulose in plant cell walls; reference to hydrogen bonding between adjacent chains; forming microfibrils; cellulose has high tensile strength, gives structural support.

Total 10 marks

EXAM QUESTION WITH MARKED STUDENT ANSWER

In living organisms small molecules are often built into large molecules, often with hundreds of small units repeated. The diagram shows the structural formulae of three such small molecules.

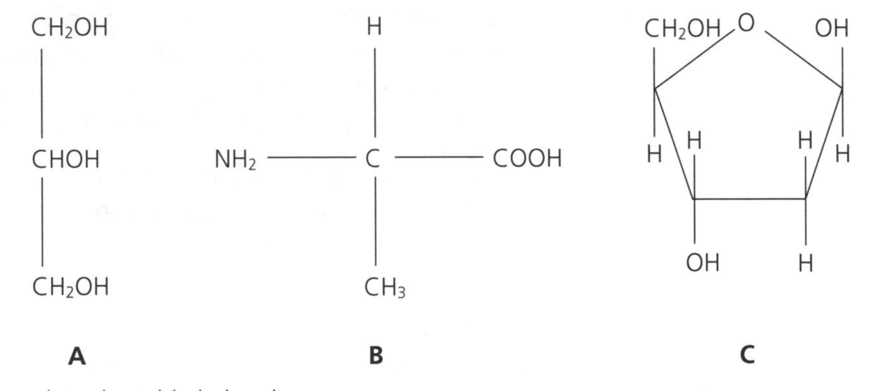

Complete the table below by

(i) naming, in each case, the molecule shown in the diagram, [3 marks]

(ii) giving the general name of a **class** of large molecules which contains the small molecule and [3 marks]

(iii) **one different** plant or animal structure which contains this large molecule. [3 marks]

Small Molecule	*Name or general name of small molecule*	*General name of a class of large molecules which contains this small molecule*	*Cell structure which contains this large molecule*
A	glycerol	lipid	membrane
B	amino acid	protein	ribosome
C	pentose	nucleic acid	DNA

"correct" (A – glycerol)

"correct" (B – amino acid)

"not enough... need 'cell' or 'plasma' as a qualification." (membrane)

"correct" (ribosome)

Total 9 marks

[WJEC]

"correct...could also have put 'monosaccharide' '5 carbon sugar' or 'deoxyribose'. All would have been correct."

"All the answers in this column are correct. For C, an alternative could have been 'nucleotide'."

"Wrong answer. Alternatives here 'chromosome' 'mitochondrion' 'chloroplast'. NB The answers in this column should refer to **structures**."

2 Genetics

SOLUTION TO REVISION ACTIVITY

1 Let B be the symbol for black coat and b the symbol for white coat.

Parents	B –	×	bb
	black female		white male
Offspring		all Bb as all are black	

The probable genotype of the female is BB as none of the offspring are white.

2

Parents	RR	×	Rr
	red		roan
Offspring	½RR		½Rr
	red		roan

There are three types of mating possible for the production of the second generation. These are ¼RR × RR, ½RR x Rr and ¼Rr × Rr.
The RR × RR mating will produce no roan offspring.
Half the matings are RR × Rr as these can be red female with roan male or roan female with red male.
Half the offspring of these matings will be roan cattle.

RR × Rr
↓
½RR ½Rr

As half the matings are of this type they will give ¼ roan in the total offspring.
One quarter of the matings are Rr x Rr. Half the offspring of these crosses will be roan.

Rr × Rr
↓
¼RR ½Rr ¼rr

Half the offspring of one quarter of the matings accounts for ⅛ of the total offspring.
The probable proportion of roan cattle in the second generation is therefore
$\frac{1}{4} + \frac{1}{8} = \frac{3}{8}$.

3 Yes. The child has the genotype I^OI^O as he has the recessive phenotype. The man is blood group B. His genotype is either I^BI^B or I^BI^O. The woman must have the genotype I^AI^O to produce a child with blood group O. If the man has the genotype I^BI^O he could be the father of the child.

4

Parents	EeVgvg			×		EeVgvg		
Gametes	EVg	Evg	eVg	evg	EVg	Evg	eVg	evg

♀ \ ♂	**EVg**	**Evg**	**eVg**	**evg**
EVg	EVg EVg	Evg EVg	eVg EVg	evg EVg
Evg	EVg Evg	Evg Evg	eVg Evg	evg Evg
eVg	EVg eVg	Evg eVg	eVg eVg	evg eVg
evg	EVg evg	Evg evg	eVg evg	evg evg

Ratio 9 wild type body colour and wings
3 wild type body colour with vestigial wings
3 ebony body with normal wings
1 ebony body with vestigial wings

256 ÷ 16 = 16

Expected progeny in each class is therefore
144 wild type body and wings
48 wild type body with vestigial wings
48 ebony body with normal wings
16 ebony body with vestigial wings

5 (a) The alleles for black and ginger are carried on the X chromosome and are co-dominant. A male cannot be tortoise-shell as this phenotype is produced by the presence of alleles for both black and ginger.
(b) Let B be the symbol for black.
Let G be the symbol for ginger.

Parents	$X^G X^G$	×	$X^B Y$
Gametes	X^G X^G		X^B Y
Offspring	$X^G X^B$		$X^G Y$
	tortoise-shell female		ginger male

ANSWERS TO EXAMINATION QUESTIONS

Question 1

(a) (i) Cell B – mitosis; no reduction in chromosome number.
Cell C – meiosis; chromosome number halved. [2 marks]

Note that both the type of cell division and the reason need to be correct for each mark.

(ii) Homologous chromosome pair;
chiasma formed or crossing over occurs;
exchange of material between chromatids. [3 marks]

(b) Any one of:
One egg cell produced but four spermatozoa;
polar bodies formed in oogenesis;
oogenesis in embryo or spermatogenesis after puberty. [1 mark]

(c) Any two of these points would gain marks:
Double fertilisation in plants;
plant embryo develops in seed / human embryo develops in uterus;
embryo has food store in plant / continuous supply via placenta in human. [2 marks]

Total 8 marks

Question 2

(a) (i) S^A 0.6 and S^B 0.4 [1 mark]
(ii) x = frequency of S^A = 0.6 y = frequency of S^B = 0.4
$x^2 + 2xy + y^2 = 1$
$(0.6 \times 0.6) + (2 \times 0.4 \times 0.6) + (0.4 \times 0.4) = 1$
$0.36\ S^A S^A + 0.48\ S^A S^B + 0.16\ S^B S^B = 1$
63 $S^A S^A$, 84 $S^A S^B$, 28 $S^B S^B$ [4 marks]

(b) (i) Haemoglobin S is abnormal and cannot carry oxygen efficiently. [1 mark]
(ii) Any two of these points would gain marks:
The heterozygous individuals do not suffer from anaemia;
they have immunity to malaria;
they have a selective advantage. [2 marks]

(c) 24–26 [1 mark]

(d) (i) Where the phenotypic character is controlled by more than one pair of alleles. [1 mark]

(ii) All the graphs, including those of the pure breeding parents, show a spread of cob length. [1 mark]

(e) (i) The two pure breeding parents show spreads of cob length that do not overlap. [1 mark]

(ii) In each parent, one genotype is giving a variety of phenotypes. [1 mark]

(f) A greater range of genotypes is produced in the F_2 generation by random assortment. [1 mark]

(g) (i) Mutation brings about the production of new alleles. [1 mark]

(ii) Synapsis occurs / bivalents are formed;
chiasmata are formed between chromatids of homologous chromatids;
new combinations of alleles are produced;
in meiosis I maternal and paternal chromosomes do not all go to the same pole.
Any of these points would gain marks. [3 marks]

Total 18 marks

Question 3

(a)

Process	***First division of meiosis***	***Mitosis***
homologous chromosomes pair	✓	✗
crossing over	✓	✗
chromatids separate	✗	✓

[3 marks]

(b) Mitosis produces genetically identical daughter cells;
meiosis does not;
with mitosis, no variation will occur in the tissue. [3 marks]

Total 6 marks

Question 4

(a) Any two of:
mental retardation; reduced resistance to disease; short stocky body;
characteristic skin folds over inner corner of the eye; heart abnormalities. [2 marks]

(b) (i) trisomy of chromosome 21 [1 mark]

(ii) any three of these points:
non-disjunction of the chromosome 21 pair;
results in a gamete containing a pair of chromosome 21;
fertilisation results in a zygote with trisomy 21;
can also occur due to 14 / 21 translocation;
most of a chromosome 21 becomes attached to a chromosome 14. [3 marks]

(c) amniocentesis
Fetal cells can be screened for the trisomy. [2 marks]

Total 8 marks

Question 5

(a) The heterozygote.
To find out which individuals in the population are carrying the allele for thalassaemia. [2 marks]

(b) Probability of an individual carrying the thalassaemia allele can be determined;
individuals can be advised of the likelihood of producing a child with thalassaemia;
may reduce the frequency of cousin marriage. [3 marks]

(c) Thalassaemia allele produced by new mutation;
will always be some carriers present in the population. [2 marks]

Total 7 marks

Question 6

(a) A reverse transcriptase
B DNA ligase [2 marks]

(b) Endonuclease makes a staggered cut;
leaves unpaired bases;
these will combine with a complementary sequence. [3 marks]

> ***Examiner's note*** The answer could also include reference to a plasmid as a vector.

(c) There are many possible answers such as:
production of insulin / clotting factors / vaccines / disease resistance in plants.
[1 mark]

Total 6 marks

EXAM QUESTION WITH MARKED STUDENT ANSWER

Models which represent the genetic material in chromosomes can be made using different coloured wires.

The drawings show four possible models made by students, only one of which is a correct representation of one pair of homologous chromosomes at metaphase of meiosis I, the first meiotic division.

The chromosomes carry an allele which occurred in two forms D and d and the model represents an individual heterozygous for this allele. No crossing over has taken place.

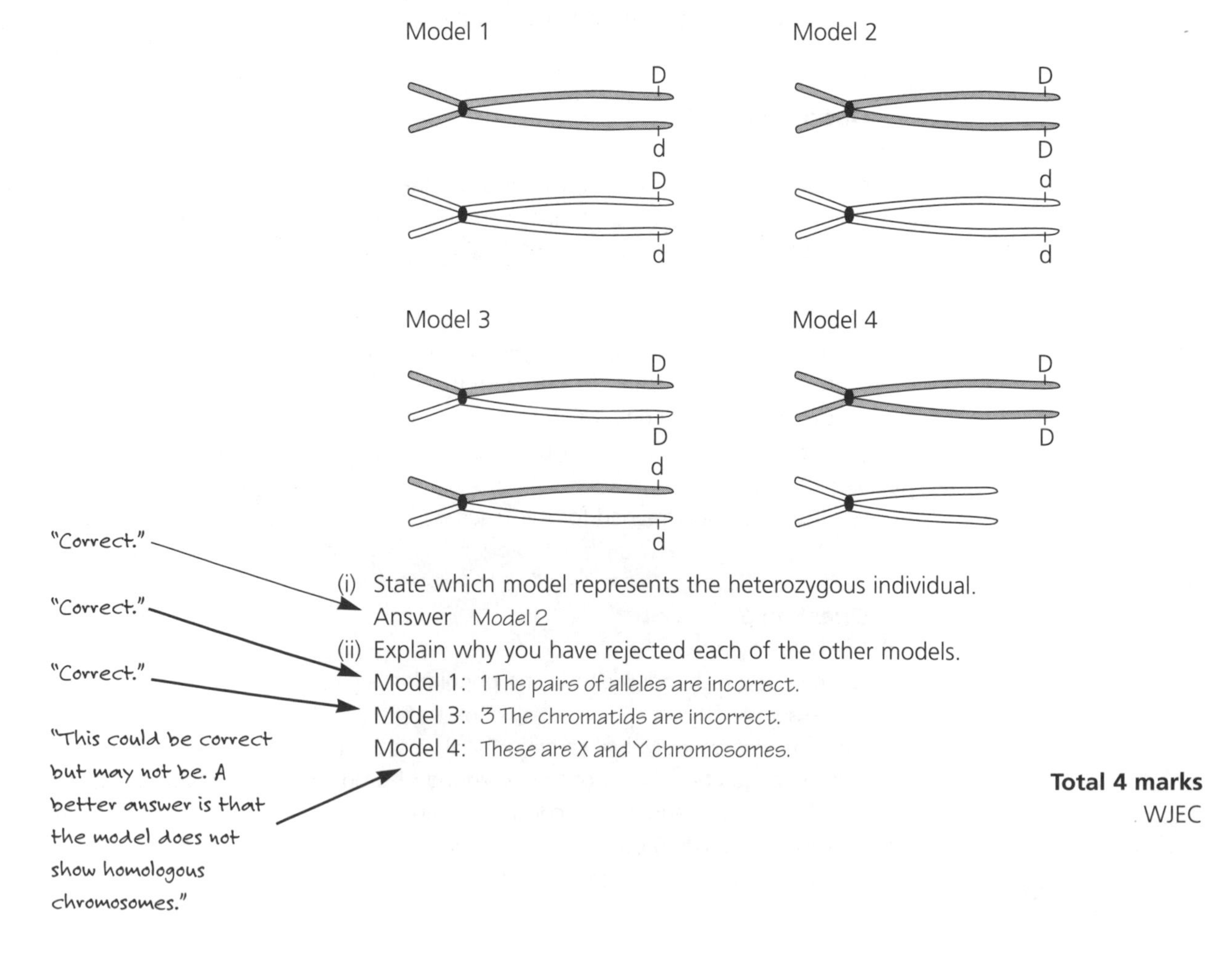

(i) State which model represents the heterozygous individual.
Answer *Model 2*

(ii) Explain why you have rejected each of the other models.
Model 1: *1 The pairs of alleles are incorrect.*
Model 3: *3 The chromatids are incorrect.*
Model 4: *These are X and Y chromosomes.*

"Correct."

"Correct."

"Correct."

"This could be correct but may not be. A better answer is that the model does not show homologous chromosomes."

Total 4 marks
WJEC

3 Enzymes and metabolic pathways

SOLUTION TO REVISION ACTIVITY

1 (a) a biological catalyst; speeds up rate of metabolic reactions
(b) specificity; does not alter reaction; does not change during reaction; reversible

2 **decarboxylases**
removal of carbon dioxide (occurs during respiration)
dehydrogenases
removal of hydrogen atoms (occurs during respiration)
hydrolases
addition of water/break bonds by addition of water (occurs during digestion)
ligases
synthesis of new bonds linking molecules (in formation of DNA, for example)
oxidases
addition of oxygen to hydrogen (occurs during respiration)
transaminases
transfer of amino groups (occurs during formation of amino acids)
transferases
transfer of atoms or groups from one molecule to another

3 inorganic ions as enzyme activators
prosthetic groups
coenzymes

4 any three of: pH; temperature; substrate concentration; enzyme concentration; presence of inhibitors; accumulation of end-product

5 active transport
muscle contraction
nerve transmission

6 (a) aerobic requires the presence of oxygen, anaerobic does not; larger amounts of energy released in aerobic
(b) in active muscle tissue where oxygen is being used up faster than it is delivered; in yeast cells deprived of oxygen

ANSWERS TO EXAMINATION QUESTIONS

Question 1

aerobic; cytoplasm; pyruvate; Krebs (or TCA); carbon dioxide; water (or H ions)

Total 6 marks

Question 2

(a) cytoplasm [1 mark] (b) glycolysis [1 mark] (c) glucose has 6, pyruvate has 3, lactate has 3 [1 mark] (d) Net gain is used because two molecules of ATP are used to phosphorylate the glucose, but four molecules of ATP are formed directly; so there is an overall gain of two molecules of ATP. [2 marks]

Total 5 marks

Question 3

(a) An enzyme is a biological catalyst; it speeds up the rate of metabolic reactions by lowering the activation energy required; does not affect the products; affected by temperature and pH; enzymes are specific, only catalysing one type of reaction.

[3 marks]

(b) Fibrous proteins have secondary structure; polypeptide chain coiled into an α helix or folded into a β pleated sheet; globular proteins have tertiary structure, the helix undergoing further folding; in globular proteins some of the R groups of the amino acids are charged or polar; attract water molecules, thus making the molecules soluble. [4 marks]

(c) The bite of the leech damages the tissues; if the active site of thrombin is blocked by hirudin, it will not be able to bring about hydrolysis of fibrinogen; so no fibrin produced and no blood clot; this enables the leech to suck up more blood than it would if clot formation was initiated; the hirudin acts as an inhibitor of thrombin. [4 marks]

Total 11 marks

Question 4

(a) (i) To absorb carbon dioxide. [1 mark]

(ii) It contains exactly the same quantities of liquid and soda lime but no yeast cells, so any fluid level differences in the manometer will be due to the activities of the yeast. [2 marks]

(b) $\frac{14.9}{50}$;

= 0.298 mm^3 of oxygen per minute [2 marks]

Total 5 marks

Question 5

(a) (i) Glycolysis occurs in the cytoplasm of respiring cells. The respiratory substrate, glucose, is first phosphorylated to make it more reactive and to prevent it from leaving the cell. The reaction is catalysed by hexokinase and uses two molecules of ATP. The phosphorylated hexose then splits to give two molecules of 3 carbon sugar, each of which is converted to glycerate-3-phosphate (GP). The glycerate-3-phosphate is converted into pyruvate. During these stages four molecules of ATP are formed and four hydrogen atoms are released. There is a net gain of two ATP and if oxygen is present, the hydrogen atoms are picked up by NAD^+ and passed along the electron carrier chain yielding more ATP. [6 marks]

(ii) If oxygen is present, pyruvate will enter a mitochondrion, where it will undergo oxidative decarboxylation, involving the removal of carbon dioxide and hydrogen. The pyruvate combines with coenzyme A to form acetyl coenzyme A. During this process, carbon dioxide and hydrogen are removed. The acetyl coenzyme A is hydrolysed and the resulting acetate (2C) combines with oxaloacetate (4C) to form citrate (6C). Dehydrogenation and decarboxylation occur, two molecules of carbon dioxide and four pairs of hydrogen atoms being removed in the reactions in which oxaloacetate is regenerated. The hydrogen atoms are accepted by NAD^+ or FAD^+ and eventually passed into the respiratory chain, generating ATP. [6 marks]

(b) ***Examiner's note*** Diagram of mitochondrion to show outer membrane, inner membrane folded to form cristae, fully labelled, would be useful here.

The matrix of the mitochondrion contains the enzymes involved in the Krebs cycle. These are separated from the cytoplasm by the mitochondrial envelope. The inner membrane is folded into projections called cristae, on which are situated the carriers of the electron transport chain. The outer membrane is permeable to small molecules, but the inner membrane is impermeable to hydrogen ions moving from outside to inside: it acts as a barrier. Respiratory chain activity results in hydrogen ions being passed along the electron transport chain from the matrix and then removed to the intermembrane space. The pH of the matrix is higher than that of the intermembrane space, so there is a difference in hydrogen ion concentration across the inner membrane. Situated on this membrane are particles which consist of a protein channel which allows hydrogen ions through and another protein (an ATPase) which uses the energy from the hydrogen ions to power the reaction that results in the formation of ATP from ADP and P_i. Because of the structure of the mitochondrion, the difference in permeability of the membranes and the location of the enzymes and electron transport chain, aerobic respiration occurs efficiently. [6 marks]

Total 18 marks

Examiner's note Not all syllabuses will require details such as are given in the answer above. You should check your syllabus to make sure you are absolutely clear about what you need to know.

Question 6

(a) (i)

Component	*Fraction number*
Mitochondria	2
Nuclei	1
Ribosomes	3

[2 marks]

(ii) Largest components sediment first/smallest last; plus some correct reference to the relative sizes of the organelles, e.g. nuclei largest. [2 marks]

(b) (i) Suspend each fraction in a buffer solution;
add succinic acid to each fraction;
incubate at a suitable (stated) temperature;
add same volume of methylene blue/TTC to each;
some correct reference to the final colour/to colour change. [4 marks]

(ii) Fraction 2/mitochondria [1 mark]

(c) TWO from:
mineral ions/glucose/enzymes/amino acids/RNA/hormones/proteins/bile salts/glycogen/urea/lipids [2 marks]

Total 11 marks

EXAM QUESTION WITH MARKED STUDENT ANSWER

The diagrams show the steps involved in the conversion of ATP and glucose into ADP and glucose phosphate.

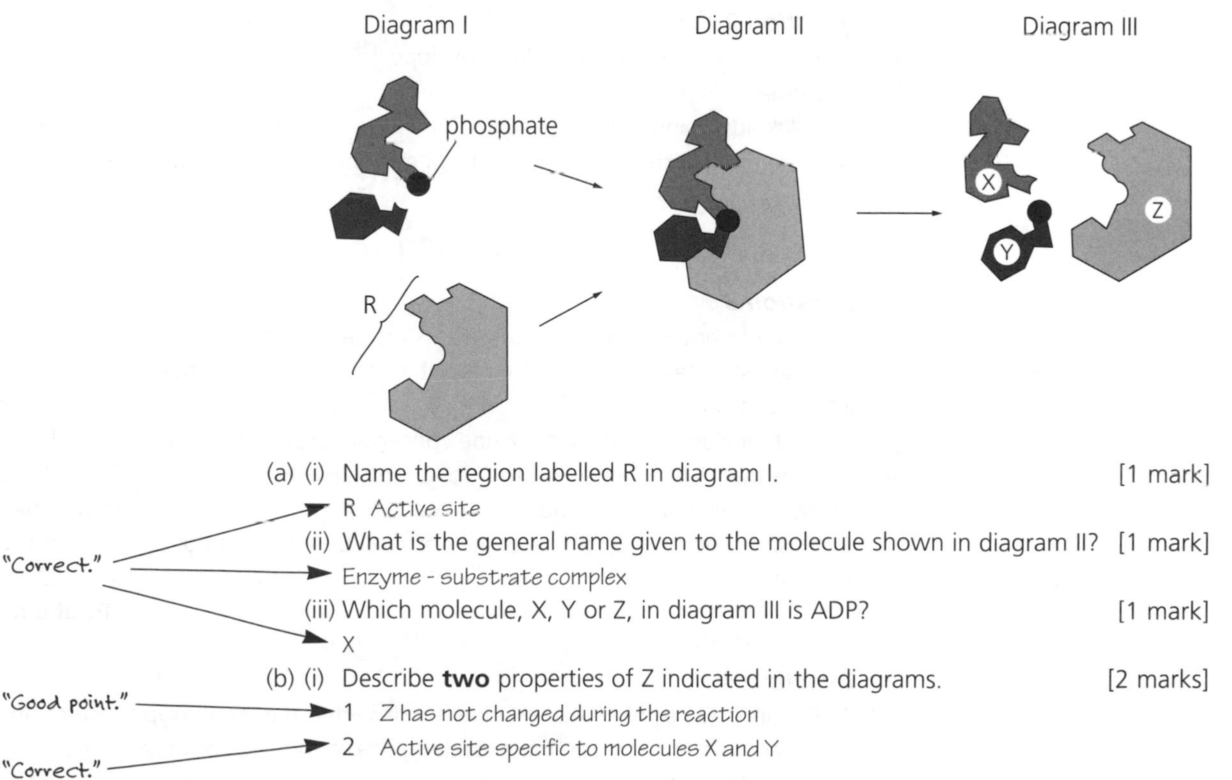

(a) (i) Name the region labelled R in diagram I. [1 mark]
R *Active site*

(ii) What is the general name given to the molecule shown in diagram II? [1 mark]
Enzyme - substrate complex

(iii) Which molecule, X, Y or Z, in diagram III is ADP? [1 mark]
X

"Correct."

(b) (i) Describe **two** properties of Z indicated in the diagrams. [2 marks]
1 *Z has not changed during the reaction* — "Good point."
2 *Active site specific to molecules X and Y* — "Correct."

"Could have put this a different way: 'Speeds up rate of reaction'."

(ii) Describe **three** other properties of Z. [3 marks]

1 lowers activation energy of the reaction

2 has an optimum pH at which it works best.

3 affected by temperature

"Good"

"Not sufficiently detailed as asked to 'Describe' so need to say how affected by temperature: 'denatured at high temperatures' OR 'works best at optimum temperatures'"

Total 8 marks

[WJEC]

4 Nutrition

SOLUTION TO REVISION ACTIVITY

(i) carotene (ii) xanthophyll (iii) red (iv) blue-violet
(v) electron (vi) electron carriers (vii) energy (viii) ATP
(ix) stroma (x) chloroplast (xi) photophosphorylation
(xii) electron (xiii) hydrogen (xiv) photolysis (xv) NADP
(xvi) Calvin (xvii) glycerate-3-phosphate
(xviii) ribulose bisphosphate (xix) glucose/hexose (xx) starch

ANSWERS TO EXAMINATION QUESTIONS

Question 1

(a) For ribulose bisphosphate, 5 in the C box and 2 in the P box.
For glycerate-3-phosphate, 3 in the C box and 1 in the P box. [1 mark]

(b) glyceraldehyde-3-phosphate [1 mark]

(c) (i) to provide energy
(i) to provide phosphate group/for phosphorylation [2 marks]

Total 4 marks

Question 2

(a) A outer membrane of chloroplast envelope
B stroma
C thylakoids/granum/granal lamellae [3 marks]

(b) Measure the length of the chloroplast in mm on the page, multiply by 1000 and divide by 2.5. [2 marks]

Total 5 marks

Question 3

(a) The rate of photosynthesis of both plants increases as the light intensity increases; increase is greatest at lower light intensities, rate of photosynthesis slows at higher light intensities. [2 marks]

(b) (i) light intensity (ii) carbon dioxide concentration/temperature [2 marks]

(c) It seems that A is better suited for growth in tropical conditions; the rate of photosynthesis is always higher and the rate continues to increase, whereas in B the curve flattens, i.e. increase in light intensity above 800 units does not cause an increase in the rate. [2 marks]

Total 6 marks

Question 4

(a) (i) Endopeptidases hydrolyse peptide bonds within the long polypeptide chains, exopeptidases hydrolyse the peptide bonds at the ends of polypeptide chains. [1 mark]

(ii) trypsin [1 mark]

(b) On the membranes of the epithelial cells [1 mark]

(c) Micro-organisms which are present in the rumen and reticulum can synthesize proteins; the micro-organisms get carried out of the rumen into the rest of the gut where protein digestion occurs, supplying the ruminant with amino acids. [2 marks]

Total 5 marks

Question 5

(a) (i) In the table, the substrate of endopeptidase is protein, and the product of exopeptidase action on polypeptides is amino acid. [2 marks]

(ii) Combined action is faster as the exopeptidases only speed up the hydrolysis of peptide bonds at the end of the polypeptide chains. [1 mark]

(b) (i) So that any effects were due to the drug only and not due to the salt solution. [1 mark]

(ii) The volume of the gall bladder continued to increase after the fat-rich meal; it doubles in size/quote figures, in the hour and a half after the meal. [2 marks]

(iii) The gall bladder does not contract and so its contents, the bile, would not be pushed into the duodenum; there would be no emulsification of the fats into tiny droplets; so there would be less efficient digestion of fats/smaller surface area for the action of lipases; might affect the action of other enzymes in the pancreatic juice as the bile is alkaline and helps to neutralise the acid contents entering the duodenum from the stomach. [2 marks]

(c) The drug appears to prevent this contraction, perhaps by blocking the effect of the hormone CCK-PZ, so fats would not be emulsified and the action of lipase in the pancreatic juice might not be as effective. [1 mark]

Total 9 marks

Question 6

(a) ***Examiner's note*** In this answer, it would be appropriate to use diagrams: a diagram of the external features of leaves and one showing the internal arrangement of the tissues could amplify the answer if they were well-labelled and annotated appropriately.

Dicotyledonous leaves are thin and flat, providing a large surface area exposed to the light and also over which gas exchange can take place. The thinness means that the diffusion paths for the gases are short, making the uptake of carbon dioxide more efficient. The leaves are usually held at right angles to the incident light by the petiole, thereby intercepting the maximum amount of light available. The midrib, main veins and network of vascular tissue provide support for the thin structure and also supply the palisade cells with water and mineral ions via the xylem. The products of photosynthesis are transported away in the phloem. With reference to the internal structure of the leaf, the palisade tissue, situated just below the transparent epidermis, contains large numbers of chloroplasts which absorb the light. These cells are columnar and packed tightly together. Beneath the palisade tissue is the spongy mesophyll, whose cells possess fewer chloroplasts, but the tissue contains large spaces through which gases can diffuse. These spaces are in connection with the stomata, pores in the lower epidermis surrounded by guard cells, through which gaseous exchange takes place. [10 marks]

(b) (i) Photosynthesis is affected by several factors and its rate is limited by that factor which is nearest its minimum value. The factors involved are light intensity, carbon dioxide concentration and temperature. If light intensity is low, an increase will increase the rate of photosynthesis up to a value where further increase has no further effect. At this point, another factor, either carbon dioxide concentration or temperature may become limiting. The reactions which occur in the light-independent stage are enzyme-controlled, so an increase in temperature could increase the rate of photosynthesis. Carbon dioxide can also be a limiting factor at this stage and an increase could increase the rate. [5 marks]

(ii) A gardener could use a greenhouse to produce more favourable conditions for photosynthesis by installing heaters to control the temperature, maintaining it at a suitable level for the crop being grown. He could also increase the carbon dioxide concentration and use lighting to maintain light intensity. The use of heating and lighting is of particular benefit when external conditions are poor. Increase in carbon dioxide concentration is of benefit all year round as the concentration in the atmosphere is quite low. [3 marks]

Total 18 marks

EXAM QUESTION WITH MARKED STUDENT ANSWER

(a) Fig. 1 shows an outline of some of the stages in the Calvin cycle.

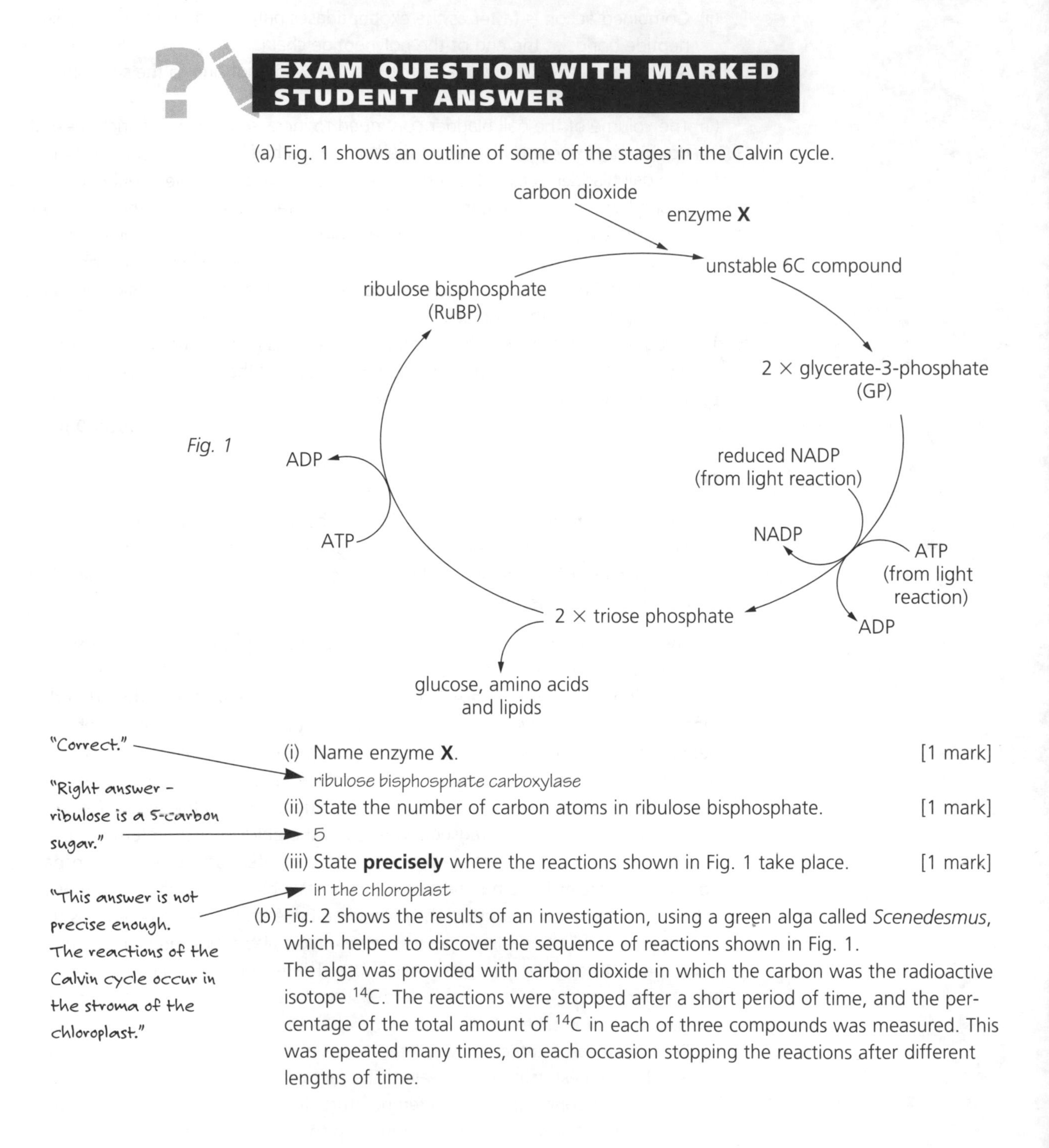

Fig. 1

(i) Name enzyme **X**. [1 mark]

ribulose bisphosphate carboxylase

"Correct."

(ii) State the number of carbon atoms in ribulose bisphosphate. [1 mark]

5

"Right answer – ribulose is a 5-carbon sugar."

(iii) State **precisely** where the reactions shown in Fig. 1 take place. [1 mark]

in the chloroplast

"This answer is not precise enough. The reactions of the Calvin cycle occur in the stroma of the chloroplast."

(b) Fig. 2 shows the results of an investigation, using a green alga called *Scenedesmus*, which helped to discover the sequence of reactions shown in Fig. 1.
The alga was provided with carbon dioxide in which the carbon was the radioactive isotope ^{14}C. The reactions were stopped after a short period of time, and the percentage of the total amount of ^{14}C in each of three compounds was measured. This was repeated many times, on each occasion stopping the reactions after different lengths of time.

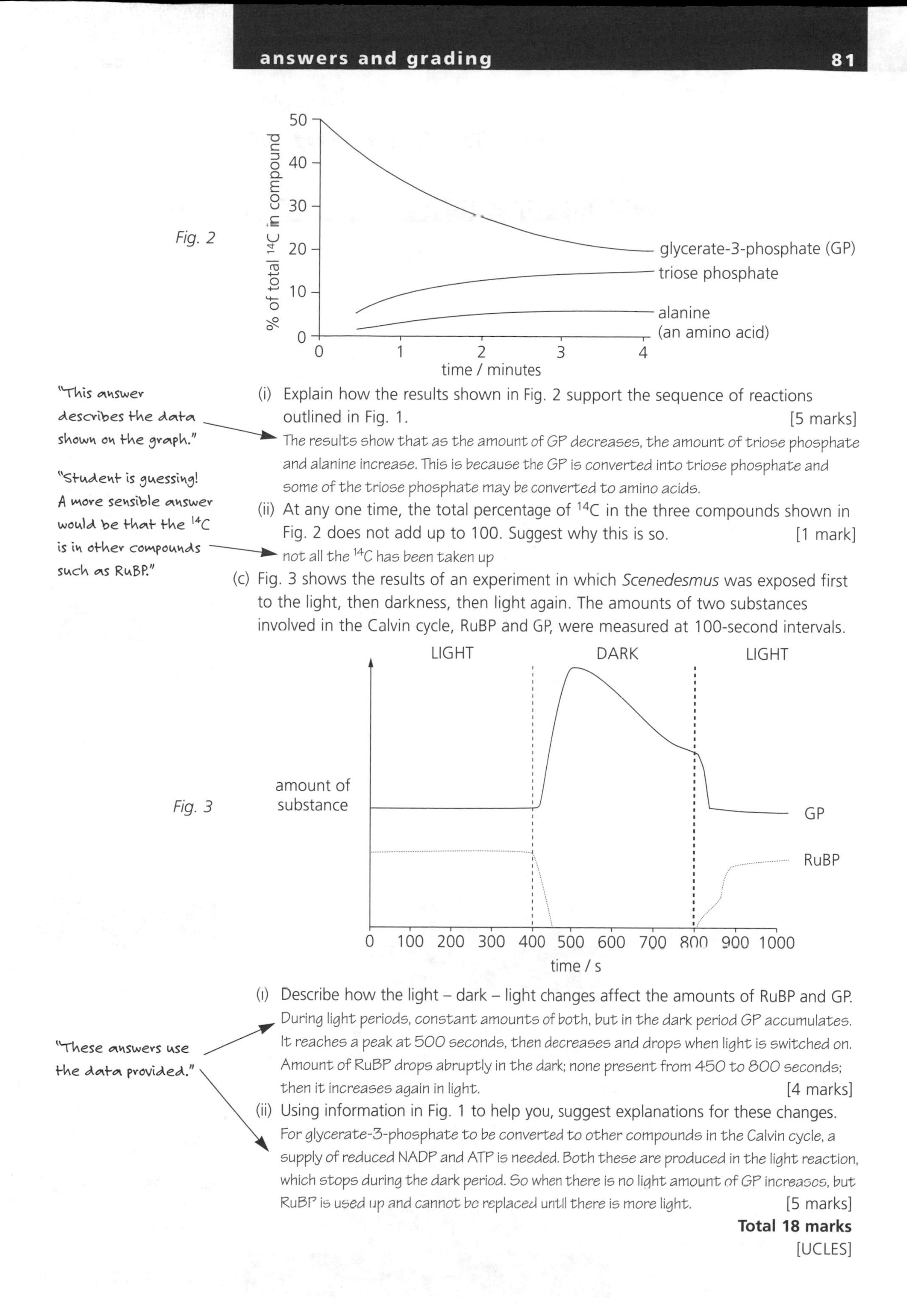

Fig. 2

"This answer describes the data shown on the graph."

(i) Explain how the results shown in Fig. 2 support the sequence of reactions outlined in Fig. 1. [5 marks]

The results show that as the amount of GP decreases, the amount of triose phosphate and alanine increase. This is because the GP is converted into triose phosphate and some of the triose phosphate may be converted to amino acids.

"Student is guessing! A more sensible answer would be that the ^{14}C is in other compounds such as RuBP."

(ii) At any one time, the total percentage of ^{14}C in the three compounds shown in Fig. 2 does not add up to 100. Suggest why this is so. [1 mark]

not all the ^{14}C has been taken up

(c) Fig. 3 shows the results of an experiment in which *Scenedesmus* was exposed first to the light, then darkness, then light again. The amounts of two substances involved in the Calvin cycle, RuBP and GP, were measured at 100-second intervals.

Fig. 3

"These answers use the data provided."

(i) Describe how the light – dark – light changes affect the amounts of RuBP and GP.

During light periods, constant amounts of both, but in the dark period GP accumulates. It reaches a peak at 500 seconds, then decreases and drops when light is switched on. Amount of RuBP drops abruptly in the dark; none present from 450 to 800 seconds; then it increases again in light. [4 marks]

(ii) Using information in Fig. 1 to help you, suggest explanations for these changes.

For glycerate-3-phosphate to be converted to other compounds in the Calvin cycle, a supply of reduced NADP and ATP is needed. Both these are produced in the light reaction, which stops during the dark period. So when there is no light amount of GP increases, but RuBP is used up and cannot be replaced until there is more light. [5 marks]

Total 18 marks

[UCLES]

5 Ecosystems and the environment

SOLUTION TO REVISION ACTIVITY

1 The appearance of your food webs will depend on your list of organisms. This is an example of a food web.

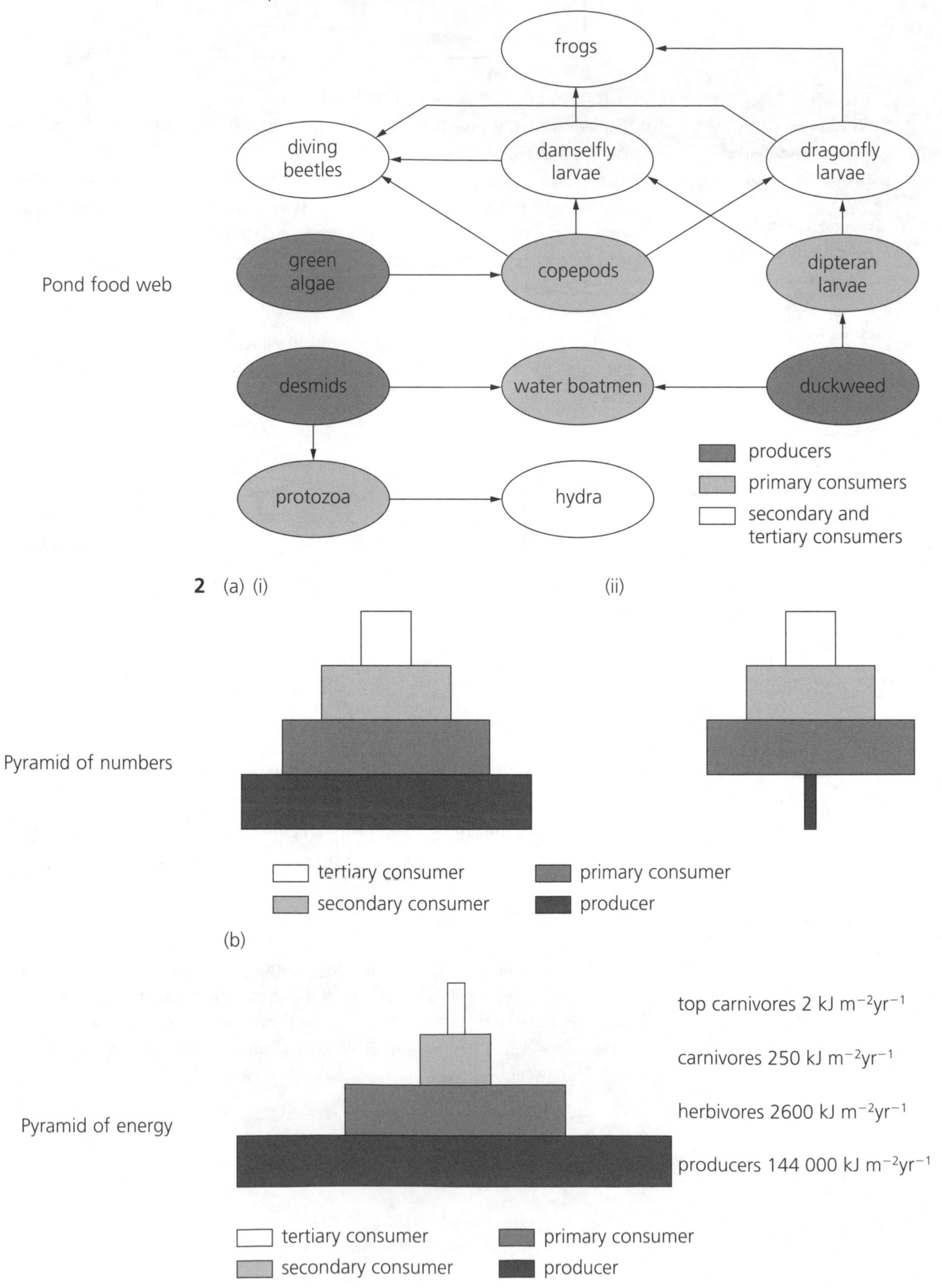

ANSWERS TO EXAMINATION QUESTIONS

Question 1

(a) 4 units of primary consumer give 1 unit of secondary consumer

$1657 \times 4 = 6628$ units

6628 units of producer biomass give 1 unit of secondary consumer biomass

[2 marks]

(b) Primary to secondary consumer in the bunchgrass system. [1 mark]

(c) (i) There is always loss of energy and therefore of biomass in transfers between trophic levels. [1 mark]

(ii) Either of the following would gain the mark:
Only a small proportion of the producer is eaten;
much of the ingested plant material is not digested and absorbed. [1 mark]

Total 5 marks

Question 2

(a) (i) A sweep net. [1 mark]

(ii) A spot of quick drying non-toxic paint;
on the ventral surface of the abdomen. [2 marks]

(b) Total population $= 50 \times \frac{54}{12}$

$= 225$ [2 marks]

(c) Any two of the following would gain full marks.

1 Food availability: if the population rises too high there is insufficient food and some will starve.
2 Predation: a rise in the population of *Notonecta* will increase the population of predators. A balance between predators and prey keeps the population of *Notonecta* stable.
3 Space: overcrowding could lead to disease or starvation, or reduce reproduction.

[4 marks]

Total 9 marks

Question 3

(a) The production of any one of proteins/nucleotides/ATP. [1 mark]

(b) Either of the following would be acceptable:
Increased use of inorganic fertilizers with consequent leaching into the water;
increased pleasure craft leading to pollution by sewage and detergents. [1 mark]

(c) (i) Increased nitrate and phosphate in the water; increased nutrients for plants increasing the plant population; increased population of primary and secondary consumers. [3 marks]

(ii) Death of large plant population; decay by aerobic micro-organisms; reduction in oxygen content of water/increase in BOD; accelerates eutrophication; leads to death of animal population.
Any three of these points would gain full marks. [3 marks]

Total 8 marks

Question 4

(a) Increase in nitrate content of the water; increase growth of algae/leads to algal bloom; death of algae and decay by aerobic micro-organisms; accelerates eutrophication; reduction in oxygen in the water/increased BOD; leads to death of the animal population.
Any four of these points would gain full marks. [4 marks]

(b) (i) Fixed nitrogen is nitrogen in compounds such as ammonia and nitrates which is available for plants. [1 mark]

(ii) Fixed nitrogen is required for the production of amino acids/nucleotides. [1 mark]

(c) (i) Little increase in leaching up to 100 mm rainfall with either surface applied or injected sludge; with higher rainfall, slow increase in leaching with surface applied sludge; rapid increase in leaching with injected sludge.
Any two of these points would gain marks. [2 marks]

(ii) The curves follow a similar pattern up to 100 mm rainfall; the difference between the curves increases rapidly as the amount of rainfall increases; uptake of fixed nitrogen by the sward; plants use that which is surface applied; little available for leaching; injected sludge not used by the plants therefore leached out by high rainfall; low rainfall leads to little percolation through the soil therefore low leaching. [4 marks]

Only four of these points would be needed, but be sure to cover both description and explanation in your answer.

(d) A farmer should apply sludge to the surface of the soil; when the rainfall is 100 mm or less. [2 marks]

Total 14 marks

Question 5

(a) Any four of the following points would gain full marks.
Stated area/size of quadrat; at each measured distance from the road; several samples at each distance; count number of each of the plant species in each quadrat; how the mean would be calculated; carry out the investigation at same season/on same day. [4 marks]

(b) (i) Any four of these points would gain marks.
Density of both decrease as move further from the main road; little change in density of either as distance from secondary road increases; mean density of A less than that of B for both roads; lower overall density of both on secondary road; same density for both at 2.5 m on main and secondary road; any relevant calculation. [4 marks]

(ii) Any two of these three points would gain marks.
Mean density of C increases further from the main road; more or less constant density along the secondary road; greater density of C than A at side of secondary road. [2 marks]

(c) (i) Any two of these points would gain marks.
Acidic gases/carbon dioxide/nitrogen oxides from vehicle exhausts; get washed into soil by rain; reference to different soil types; more traffic on the main road than the secondary road. [2 marks]

(ii) Any two of these points would gain marks.
A and B can tolerate/prefer low pH so A and B at greater density along main road; C not tolerant to low pH; pH tolerance less important further away from main road; less variation in pH along secondary road so C competes better. [2 marks]

(iii) Reference to any sensible suggestion, for example other toxic chemicals/lead/herbicide/salt/trampling/cutting management. [1 mark]

Total 15 marks

Question 6

(a) (i) **S** *Rhizobium/Azotobacter/Anabaena/Clostridium*
T *Pseudomonas/Bacillus/Thiobacillus* [2 marks]

(ii) **X** decomposition/putrefaction/decay/deamination
Y denitrification [2 marks]

(b) Any of these three points would gain full marks.
Nitrates are soluble/leach out of soil; stimulate plant growth; cause excessive plant growth/algal bloom then die; decay by aerobic bacteria which increase; oxygen levels decrease/raised BOD. [3 marks]

Total 7 marks

EXAM QUESTION WITH MARKED STUDENT ANSWER

The diagram shows the energy flow and trophic levels in a temperate deciduous forest. The units for the numbers given are in kJ m^{-2} day^{-1}.

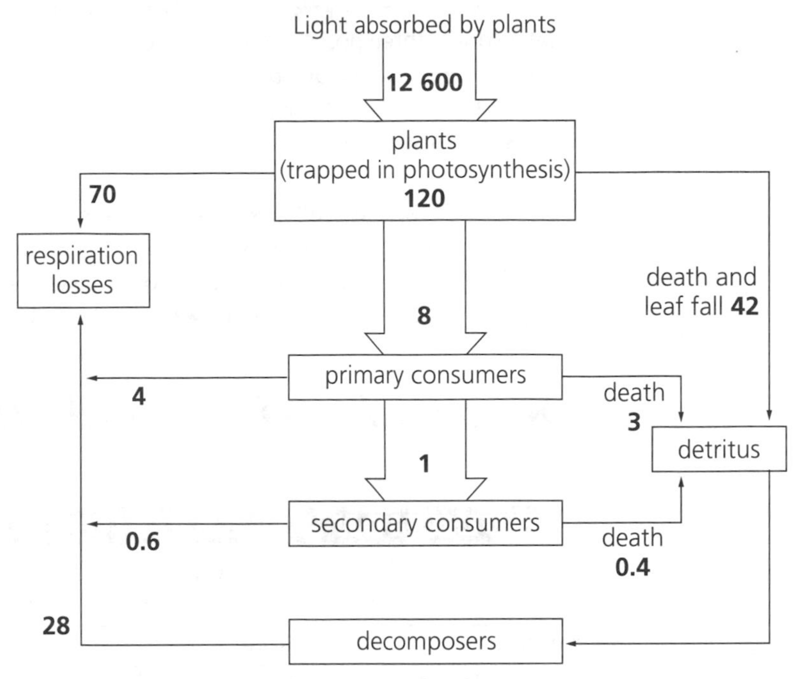

The net primary production of the plants in this ecosystem is equal to the energy fixed by plants and available to consumers. This is represented by the following formula.

Net primary production = Gross primary production − Respiration losses.
(energy trapped by plants in photosynthesis)

(a) Calculate the percentage of net primary production that becomes plant detritus. Show your working.

42/50 × 100

= 84% [2 marks]

"Correct."

"This is worth one mark."

(b) State what is meant by the term trophic level.

A trophic level is a feeding level in a food chain. [1 mark]

"Correct."

(c) Explain how energy pyramids can provide information about the transfer of energy between trophic levels.

Energy pyramids show the amount of energy in each trophic level.

Each has less than the one below it. [2 marks]

"There should also be a comment about how energy is lost from each trophic level, e.g. by respiration or excretion or some organisms or parts of organisms not being eaten."

(d) (i) Complete the pyramid to show the second trophic level drawn to the same scale. [1 mark]

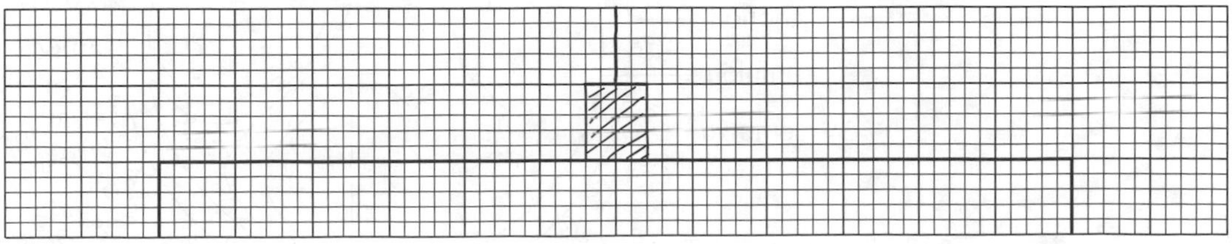

"Correct. It is to scale and drawn centrally."

Energy flow / kJ m^{-2} day^{-1}

(ii) Between which trophic levels does the greater decrease in energy flow occur? Give two reasons for your answer.

Between levels 1 and 2.

Not all the plant biomass is eaten.

Some of the ingested material is not incorporated into the primary consumer, it is lost as faeces. [3 marks]

"It would have been better to give a comparative statement. A smaller percentage of the plant biomass is eaten than the percentage of the primary consumers. A larger proportion of the plant biomass is not digested. A comment could have been made that a larger percentage of the energy taken in by the plant is lost in respiration."

(e) Suggest three possible consequences of the removal of trees from the forest.

1 A major source of food for primary consumers is removed.
2 Many ecological niches will be lost.
3 The water table will be changed. [3 marks]

Total 12 marks

[UCLES]

"These are all correct. Other points that could have been made are: new communities develop in the space produced; shade loving plants may disappear; the overall productivity of the forest will be reduced; some food chains may be lost."

6 Reproduction and development

SOLUTION TO REVISION ACTIVITY

1

Hormone	***Roles***
Follicle stimulating hormone	In male, stimulates spermatogenesis. In female, growth of ovarian follicles.
Luteinizing hormone	In male, testosterone secretion. In female, secretion of oestrogen and progesterone, ovulation, maintenance of corpus luteum.
Oestrogen	Female secondary sexual characteristics, oestrus cycle.
Progesterone	Inhibition of ovulation, maintenance of gestation.
Chorionic gonadotrophin	Maintenance of corpus luteum.
Testosterone	Male secondary sexual characteristics.
Prolactin	Stimulation of milk production.
Oxytocin	Release of milk from breast, contraction of uterus during birth.

2

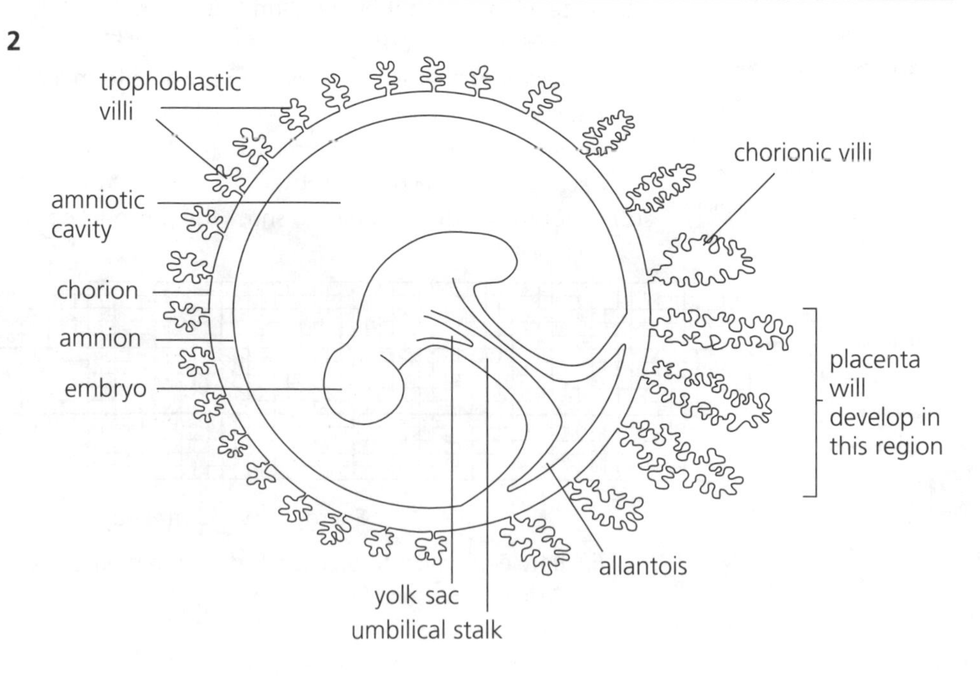

3

Wind pollinated	*Insect pollinated*
Petals small or absent	Petals large and coloured
Not scented	Scented
No nectaries	Nectaries
Large feathery stigma hanging out of the flower	Small sticky stigma within the flower
Stamens pendulous and hanging out of the flower	Stamens within the flower
Anthers loosely attached to filament	Anthers firmly attached to filament
Pollen grains plentiful and light	Less pollen produced and relatively heavy
Pollen smooth and dry	Pollen spiny and/or sticky

ANSWERS TO EXAMINATION QUESTIONS

Question 1

FSH; oestrogen; endometrium / uterine lining; secondary oocyte; corpus luteum; progesterone

Total 6 marks

Question 2

(a) Large numbers of genetically identical cells are produced; these give rise to primary spermatocytes which produce spermatozoa by meiosis. [2 marks]

(b) Any two of these points would gain full marks.
It is the acrosome and its outer membrane ruptures; releasing enzymes / proteases / hyaluronidase; digest the cell layers surrounding the oocyte; inner membrane of the acrosome everts to allow penetration of the zona pellucida. [2 marks]

(c) Either of these would gain the marks.
Fertilisation can take place without resort to an aquatic environment, the necessary fluid is provided by the female tract; fertilisation is more likely to occur and fewer sperm and eggs need to be produced as the sperm and egg are contained within a limited space. [2 marks]

Total 6 marks

Question 3

(a) (i) **A** oogonium **B** primary oocyte **C** secondary oocyte **D** first polar body [2 marks]

(ii) produced in the fetus; in the germinal epithelium of the ovary. [2 marks]

(b) A has the diploid number of chromosomes, C is haploid.
Cells E and F are both haploid. [2 marks]

(c) In oogenesis, one ovum is produced from a primary oocyte; in spermatogenesis, four spermatozoa are produced from a primary spermatocyte;
polar bodies are produced in oogenesis;
primary oocytes are produced in the fetus;
primary spermatocytes are only produced after puberty;
maturation of spermatozoa is continuous, maturation of ova is cyclical;
meiosis is only completed in ova after fertilisation.
Any four of these points would gain the marks. [4 marks]

Total 10 marks

Question 4

(a) **A** scion **B** stock [2 marks]

(b) Makes the join secure;
large surface area for contact between the tissues. [2 marks]

(c) Any two of these points would gain the marks.
Maintains the genetic make up / sure to get the variety you want;
apple trees are difficult to grow from seed;
fruit produced more quickly;
can control the size of the tree by choice of root stock;
root stock can give disease resistance. [2 marks]

Total 6 marks

Question 5

(a) (i) Day 5 to 27 the follicle grows slowly to day 24, then rapidly; sudden decrease in size on day 27 as the ovum is released from the follicle. [2 marks]
(ii) Primary follicle grows under the influence of FSH;
LH controls the later development of the follicle;
interaction of LH, FSH and prostaglandins brings about ovulation. [3 marks]
(b) (i) Three cycles of ovulation took place.
(ii) Both corpora lutea diminished in size during the period. [2 marks]
(c) Arrow to one of the three falls in the follicle diameter graph. [1 mark]

Total 8 marks

Question 6

(a) Transfer of pollen from the anthers of one flower;
to the stigma of another flower of the same species. [2 marks]
(b) Any four of these points would gain the marks.
remove anthers from the flower of one variety;
to prevent self-pollination / before pollen matures;
transfer pollen by hand;
to stigmas of emasculated flowers;
when stigmas / carpels have developed;
after pollination keep flower covered until seeds develop. [4 marks]

Total 6 marks

EXAM QUESTION WITH MARKED STUDENT ANSWER

Records of human fertility for the period 1930 to 1990 have shown changes in the sperm counts of normal men.
The table below summarizes the changing percentages of men with high or low sperm counts over a period of sixty years.

High sperm count $< 100 \times 10^6$ sperm cm^{-3}
Low sperm count $> 20 \times 10^6$ sperm cm^{-3}

Time period	*Men with high sperm counts / %*	*Men with low sperm counts / %*
1930–1950	50	5
1951–1960	45	4
1961–1970	28	14
1971–1980	21	11
1981–1990	15	18

(a) (i) Comment on the changes in the percentage of men with high sperm counts during the period 1930–1990.

The percentage is falling throughout the period.
The largest fall is between 1960 and 1970. [2 marks]

"These comments are both correct. Reference could have been made to the fall in percentage flattening off from 1970."

(ii) Compare the figures for men with low sperm counts with those with high sperm counts over the same period.

The percentage of men with low sperm counts is much lower at the beginning. The fall in percentage of men with high sperm counts is greater than the rise in percentage of men with low sperm counts. [3 marks]

"These comparisons are correct but only two points have been made and so full marks would not be obtained.
Other points that could have been made are: the numbers are increasing during the period ; the largest rise is in the 1960s; the numbers of men with low sperm counts fluctuate after 1980."

(b) Explain why it is necessary for large numbers of sperms to be produced when only one sperm is required to bring about fertilisation.

Large numbers of sperm fail to reach the Fallopian tubes, because they are abnormal or have reduced motility. [2 marks]

"These are two good points. Marks could also have been obtained by stating that conditions in the vagina are hostile to sperm or that large numbers of sperm are needed to produce the enzymes needed to digest the outer membranes of the egg cell."

(c) Exposure of pregnant women to high levels of certain oestrogens during early pregnancy can result in reproductive disorders in their male offspring.

It appears that a number of compounds in the environment can mimic the action of oestrogens when ingested. Such compounds, termed oestrogenic chemicals, are found in pesticides such as DDT and PCBs and also in the breakdown products of certain detergents. They accumulate in the fatty tissue and have the same effect as oestrogens, which play a major role in the menstrual cycle.

(i) Describe the normal role of oestrogens in the menstrual cycle.

They repair the wall of the uterus. Increasing levels of oestrogen inhibit FSH production and stimulate the production of LH. [3 marks]

"This is not correct. Reference should be made to the endometrium or uterine lining being repaired."

"These two points are correct. Reference could also have been made to increasing levels leading to ovulation."

(ii) Suggest how the oestrogenic chemicals pass from the mother to the developing fetus.

They pass into the fetus from the mother via the umbilical cord in the blood stream. [3 marks]

"This would not gain marks, the answer is too imprecise. Reference is needed to uptake from the maternal blood to the fetal blood by diffusion from the placenta.
Reference could also be made to mobilisation from the body fat."

"Reference is needed to the umbilical vein, not the umbilical cord."

Total 13 marks

[[London]]

7 Support, locomotion and transport

SOLUTION TO REVISION ACTIVITY

(a) The structures labelled 1 to 14:

1 Right atrium	2 Right ventricle	3 Pulmonary artery
4 Papillary muscle	5 Tricuspid valve	6 Tendinous cords
7 Interventricular septum	8 Semilunar valve	9 Left ventricle
10 Bicuspid valve	11 Left atrium	12 Aorta
13 Pulmonary vein	14 Vena cava	

(b) The differences between:

A and **B** after a meal:

A represents the hepatic portal vein carrying blood from the small intestine to the liver. There will be more glucose, amino acids and other products of digestion in **A** than in **B**. Remember that vitamins and mineral ions are not digested but are absorbed in this region of the gut. After a meal the level of glucose in the blood will be high, so there will also be a higher level of insulin. Check your knowledge of insulin and its importance.

C and **D**:

These vessels are the renal artery and renal vein respectively. The renal vein will contain less urea than the renal artery. The water content of the blood may be different – check you know the function of the kidney in osmoregulation. The blood in **D** will also contain less glucose, less oxygen and more carbon dioxide due to the respiratory activity of the kidney tissue.

A and **E**:

E is the hepatic vein and the concentration of a large number of metabolites will have been regulated by the activities of the liver. The level of glucose in the blood is regulated here, as is the level of some vitamins and mineral ions, iron is stored and excess protein is deaminated so the blood in **E** will contain more urea. You should check your syllabus to find out how much you need to know about the functions of the liver.

F and **G**:

F is the vena cava and is the main vein returning deoxygenated blood to the heart. **G** is the pulmonary vein and returns blood to the heart from the lungs, so will contain more oxygen and less carbon dioxide than **F**.

ANSWERS TO EXAMINATION QUESTIONS

Question 1

Statement	*Xylem vessels*	*Phloem sieve tubes*
Possess living contents	✗	✓
Provide support	✓	✗
Composed of cells fused together end to end	✓	✓
Walls contain lignin	✓	✗

Total 4 marks

Question 2

(a) (i) **B** (ii) **C** [2 marks]

(b) (i) Standing on a sharp stone will stimulate sensory receptor in the foot. Nerve impulses will travel via sensory neurone to the cell body in the dorsal root ganglion and then to the grey matter of the spinal cord. The sensory neurone will synapse with a relay neurone, which relays the stimulus to a motor neurone. The motor neurone transmits the impulse to the muscle **A**, which is stimulated to contract, bending the leg at the knee and removing the foot from the stone. [3 marks]

(ii) Prevents damage to the body. [1 mark]

Total 6 marks

Question 3

(a) (i) Neither require energy from ATP/in both, molecules move from high concentration to lower concentration. [1 mark]

(ii) in facilitated diffusion a protein carrier is involved [1 mark]

(b) (i) high (ii) high (iii) low [1 mark]

(c) (i) Increase in temperature increases movement of ions, so diffusion faster. [1 mark]

(ii) Respiratory poison will stop production of ATP, so active transport of the sodium ions can no longer occur. [1 mark]

Total 5 marks

Question 4

(a) The endothelium is the inner layer and is only one cell thick in both blood vessels. [1 mark]

(b) The artery is vessel **A**, because it has a greater thickness of smooth muscle and elastic tissue than vessel **B**. [2 marks]

(c) Veins have semilunar valves, which prevent the backflow of blood. Upward pressure of the blood keeps the valves open, but they close if the pressure drops, preventing the flow in the opposite direction. [2 marks]

Total 5 marks

Question 5

(a) (i) **A** sino-atrial node (ii) **C** bundle of His in the interventricular septum [2 marks]

(b) **B** is the atrio-ventricular node, through which the wave of excitation is passed to the ventricles, causing them to contract. The time delay allows the contraction of the atria to be completed before the contraction of the ventricles begins. [2 marks]

(c) The wave of excitation passes from **A** over the atria and takes 0.09 seconds to reach **D**. The excitation does not leave **B** until 0.07 seconds after it reaches **D**. On leaving **B**, the wave of excitation is conducted along the bundle of His and along the Purkinje tissue in the ventricles. This wave of excitation reaches point **E** 0.03 seconds after it leaves **B** and 0.10 seconds after it reaches **D**. The wave of excitation, which stimulates the contraction of the ventricles from the apex upwards, can only pass along the interventricular septum which is why there is a delay of 0.03 seconds between **B** and **E**. [2 marks]

(d) The muscular wall of the left ventricle is three times thicker than that of the right ventricle and the more powerful contraction results in the much higher pressure of the blood leaving the left ventricle. Blood leaving the right ventricle only supplies the pulmonary circulation, whereas blood from the left ventricle supplies the systemic circulation. [2 marks]

(e) Cardiac output is equal to the amount of blood expelled at each beat multiplied by the heart rate. The pacemaker (sino-atrial node) determines the rate at which the heart beats and this can be affected by the sympathetic nervous system. Stimulation of the sympathetic system causes the heart rate to increase and this would increase the cardiac output. [3 marks]

Total 11 marks

Question 6

(a) (i) **A** I band **B** H zone **C** Z line [3 marks]

(ii) myosin [1 mark]

(b) becomes shorter/narrower/smaller [1 mark]

Total 5 marks

EXAM QUESTIONS WITH MARKED STUDENT ANSWER

The diagram shows a motor end plate.

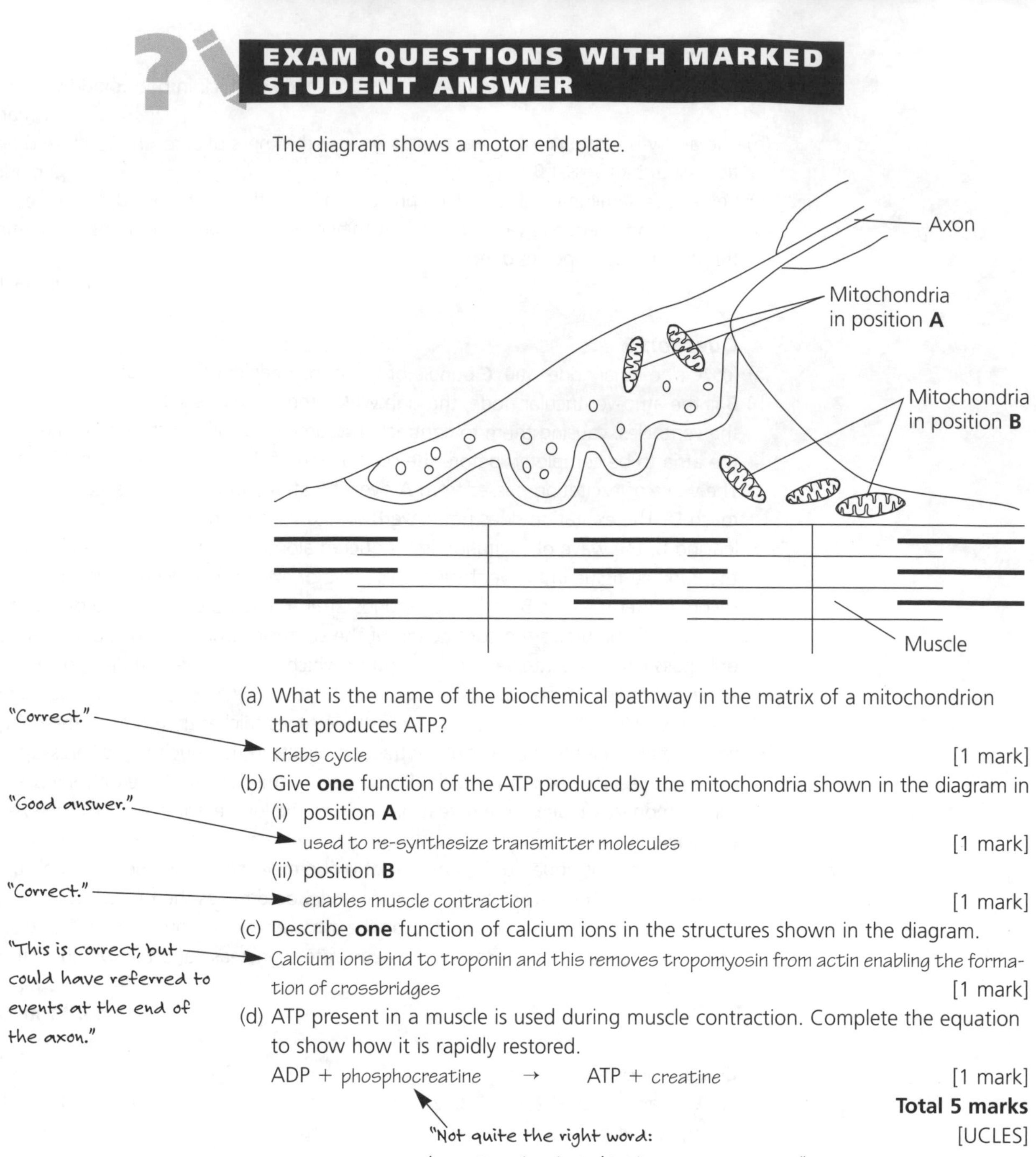

(a) What is the name of the biochemical pathway in the matrix of a mitochondrion that produces ATP?

Krebs cycle [1 mark]

"Correct."

(b) Give **one** function of the ATP produced by the mitochondria shown in the diagram in

(i) position **A**

used to re-synthesize transmitter molecules [1 mark]

"Good answer."

(ii) position **B**

enables muscle contraction [1 mark]

"Correct."

(c) Describe **one** function of calcium ions in the structures shown in the diagram.

Calcium ions bind to troponin and this removes tropomyosin from actin enabling the formation of crossbridges [1 mark]

"This is correct, but could have referred to events at the end of the axon."

(d) ATP present in a muscle is used during muscle contraction. Complete the equation to show how it is rapidly restored.

ADP + *phosphocreatine* → ATP + *creatine* [1 mark]

"Not quite the right word: 'creatine phosphate' is the correct answer."

Total 5 marks

[UCLES]

8 Coordination and homeostasis

SOLUTION TO REVISION ACTIVITY

1 (i) Anterior pituitary

FSH	In male, stimulates spermatogenesis. In female, stimulates growth of ovarian follicles.
LH	In male stimulates testosterone secretion. In female stimulates secretion of oestrogen and progesterone, involved in ovulation and maintenance of the corpus luteum.
Prolactin	Stimulates milk production and secretion
TSH	Brings about synthesis and secretion of thyroxine.
ACTH	Stimulates synthesis and secretion of glucocorticoids and aldosterone by adrenal cortex.
Growth hormone	Protein synthesis and growth, especially of bones and limbs.

(ii) Thyroid gland

Thyroxine	Regulation of basal metabolic rate, growth and development.
Calcitonin	Decreases blood calcium level.

(iii) Islets of Langerhans

Insulin (β cells)	Decreases blood glucose level, increases glucose and amino acid uptake by cells.
Glucagon (α cells)	Increases blood glucose level; breakdown of glycogen to glucose in the liver.

(iv) Adrenal medulla

Glucocorticoids	Protein breakdown, adaptation to stress, anti-inflammatory effects.
Aldosterone	Sodium retention in the kidney, controls sodium and potassium ratios in body fluids, raises blood pressure.

2

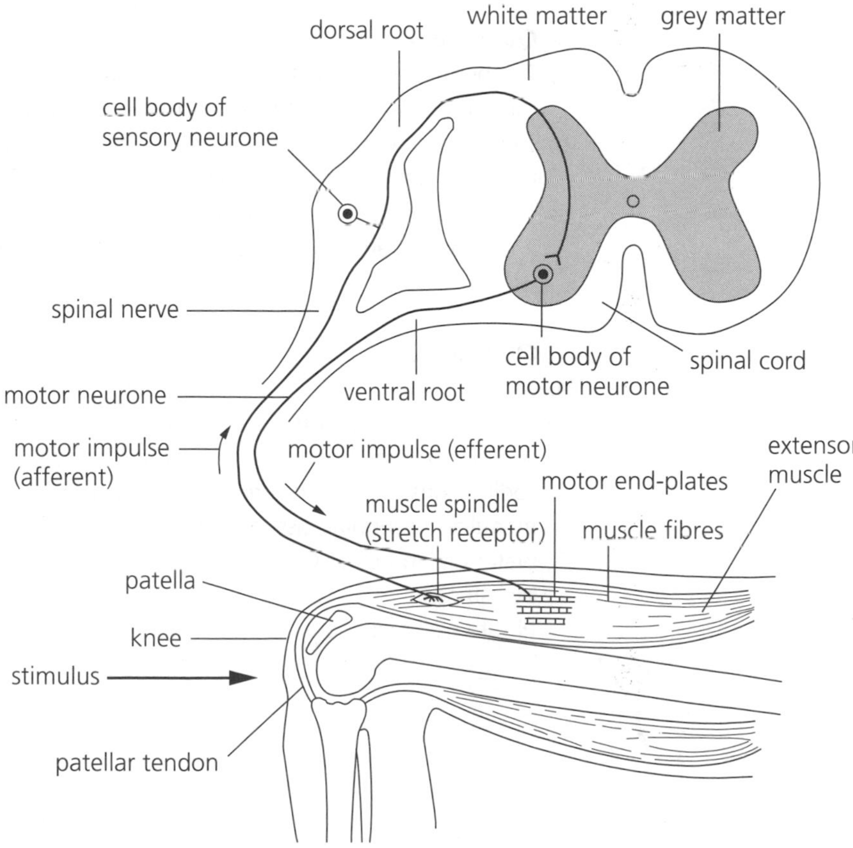

Spinal reflex arc

3 **Experiment 1** Put coleoptiles in unidirectional light and the tips bend towards the light. Put another set of coleoptiles, with tips covered, in unidirectional light and they do not bend towards the light. The conclusion is that the tip detects the light stimulus.
Experiment 2 Mica strips should be inserted half way across the coleoptiles just below the tips. The coleoptiles are then placed in unidirectional light. If the mica insert is on the same side as the light source, the coleoptile bends towards the light. If the mica insert is on the opposite side, the coleoptile does not bend. The conclusion is that a growth-promoting substance is produced by the tip and is prevented from travelling down the dark side of the coleoptile by the mica strip.
Experiment 3 The tips are removed from the coleoptiles and placed on agar blocks. If a block is placed centrally on the decapitated coleoptile, the coleoptile grows upwards. If the block is placed to one side, the coleoptile bends towards the opposite side. The conclusion is that a growth substance has diffused from the tip into the agar block. When the block is placed on the decapitated coleoptile, growth is induced.

ANSWERS TO EXAMINATION QUESTIONS

Question 1

(a) (i) negative feedback [1 mark]
(ii) A meal has been eaten and glucose has been absorbed into the blood from the small intestine. [1 mark]
(iii) It binds with a receptor site and alters the permeability of the cell membrane to glucose. [1 mark]
(b) (i) It stimulates the synthesis of amylase;
this breaks down starch to maltose and the maltose is broken down into glucose by maltase. [2 marks]
(ii) There is no regulation or feedback mechanism. [1 mark]
Total 6 marks

Question 2

(a) The permeability of the membrane to sodium ions increases momentarily;
this increases the number of positive ions inside the axon. [2 marks]
(b) To repolarise the membrane, sodium ions must be pumped out;
this is an active process involving energy from ATP. [2 marks]
(c) This will reduce the potential difference across the membrane;
if the concentration is lowered sufficiently, an action potential will not occur. [2 marks]
Total 6 marks

Question 3

(a) (i) 99.17% (ii) 0.0 g (iii) 28 g (iv) 52.8% [4 marks]
(b) Any four of these would gain full marks.
Ascending limb impermeable to water/permeable to sodium ions;
sodium ions pumped out/moved out by active transport;
medulla/surrounding tissue more concentrated than filtrate;
water drawn out of **Q**/descending limb/distal convoluted tubule;
by osmosis;
filtrate becomes more concentrated in **Q**. [3 marks]
Total 7 marks

Question 4

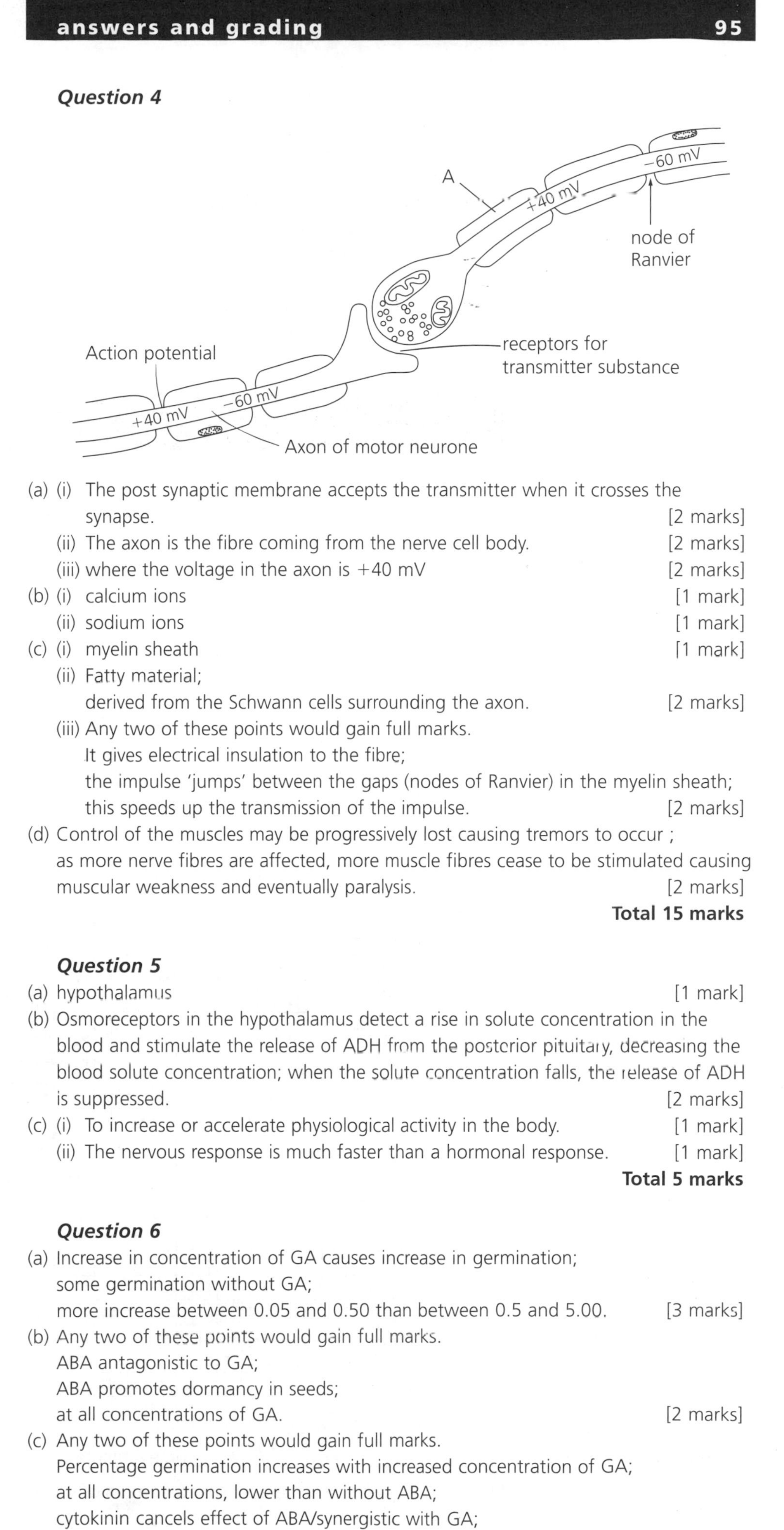

(a) (i) The post synaptic membrane accepts the transmitter when it crosses the synapse. [2 marks]
(ii) The axon is the fibre coming from the nerve cell body. [2 marks]
(iii) where the voltage in the axon is +40 mV [2 marks]
(b) (i) calcium ions [1 mark]
(ii) sodium ions [1 mark]
(c) (i) myelin sheath [1 mark]
(ii) Fatty material;
derived from the Schwann cells surrounding the axon. [2 marks]
(iii) Any two of these points would gain full marks.
It gives electrical insulation to the fibre;
the impulse 'jumps' between the gaps (nodes of Ranvier) in the myelin sheath;
this speeds up the transmission of the impulse. [2 marks]
(d) Control of the muscles may be progressively lost causing tremors to occur ;
as more nerve fibres are affected, more muscle fibres cease to be stimulated causing muscular weakness and eventually paralysis. [2 marks]

Total 15 marks

Question 5

(a) hypothalamus [1 mark]
(b) Osmoreceptors in the hypothalamus detect a rise in solute concentration in the blood and stimulate the release of ADH from the posterior pituitary, decreasing the blood solute concentration; when the solute concentration falls, the release of ADH is suppressed. [2 marks]
(c) (i) To increase or accelerate physiological activity in the body. [1 mark]
(ii) The nervous response is much faster than a hormonal response. [1 mark]

Total 5 marks

Question 6

(a) Increase in concentration of GA causes increase in germination;
some germination without GA;
more increase between 0.05 and 0.50 than between 0.5 and 5.00. [3 marks]
(b) Any two of these points would gain full marks.
ABA antagonistic to GA;
ABA promotes dormancy in seeds;
at all concentrations of GA. [2 marks]
(c) Any two of these points would gain full marks.
Percentage germination increases with increased concentration of GA;
at all concentrations, lower than without ABA;
cytokinin cancels effect of ABA/synergistic with GA;
still no germination when no GA present. [2 marks]

(d) (i) light / oxygen / pH [1 mark]

(ii) Any two of these points would gain full marks.
Vary the concentration of ABA;
vary the concentration of CK;
use concentrations of GA between 0.50 and 5.00;
use higher concentrations of GA;
use CK only;
use ABA and CK together;
use other varieties of seeds. [2 marks]

Total 10 marks

EXAM QUESTION WITH MARKED STUDENT ANSWER

An experiment was carried out to investigate the relationship between the concentrations of glucose and insulin in the blood of healthy people. At the start of this experiment 34 volunteers each ingested a syrup containing 50 g of glucose. The concentration of glucose and insulin was determined in blood samples at intervals over a period of 2 hours. The results shown in the graph below are mean values for the group of volunteers.

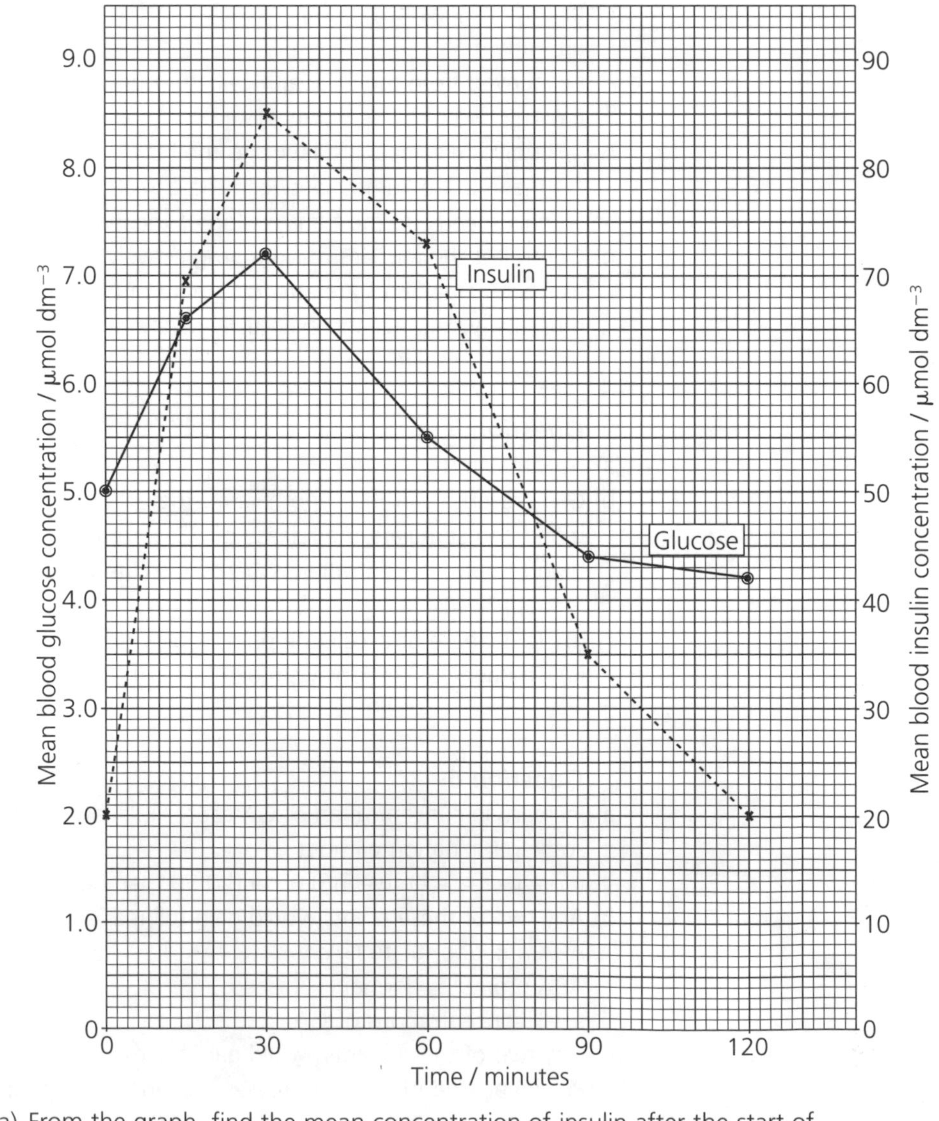

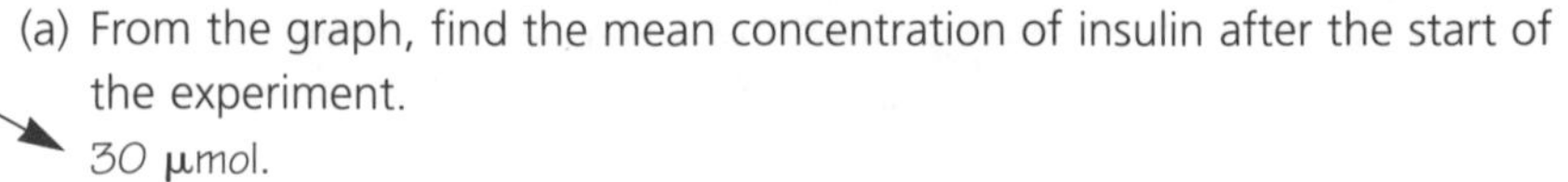

(a) From the graph, find the mean concentration of insulin after the start of the experiment.

30 µmol. [1 mark]

"This would not gain a mark as the units are incorrect. The answer is 30 µmol dm^{-3}."

"This is correct. Credit could also be gained from quoting figures from the graph."

"This is correct. Credit could also be gained by the use of figures or stating that the final concentration is lower than the starting concentration."

(b) Comment on the changes in the concentration of glucose during the following time intervals.

(i) 0 to 30 minutes — The blood glucose concentration increases due to absorption from the gut. [2 marks]

(ii) 30 to 120 minutes — The blood glucose level decreases rapidly due to uptake by the liver. [2 marks]

(c) Comment on the relationship between the concentrations of glucose and insulin as shown by this graph.

Both concentrations increase up to 30 minutes. They then decrease.
The rise in glucose stimulates insulin secretion. This is a positive feedback regulation.

[3 marks]

"This is a good answer, stating what happens and giving an explanation why."

(d) Name one hormone, other than insulin, which is involved with the regulation of blood glucose and state its effect on blood glucose concentration.

Hormone glucagon

Effect it increases the blood glucose concentration. [2 marks]

Total 10 marks

[London]

"This is correct. Other acceptable answers would be thyroxine decreasing the level, glucocorticoids increasing the level or adrenalin increasing the level."

part IV

Timed practice papers with answers

Timed practice papers

TIMED PRACTICE PAPER 1

Structured questions
This paper should be completed in 60 minutes.
The total mark for the paper is 50 marks.

Question 1

The table below refers to events in the processes of mitosis and the first division of meiosis (meiosis I).
If the statement is correct, place a tick (✓) in the appropriate box and if the statement is incorrect place a cross (✗) in the appropriate box.

Feature	*Mitosis*	*Meiosis I*
Formation of spindle occurs		
Homologous chromosomes pair up		
Separation of chromatids occurs		
Formation of chiasmata		
Condensation of chromosomes		

Total 5 marks
[London]

Question 2

Read through the following account of protein synthesis, then write on the dotted lines the most appropriate word or words to complete the account.

During protein synthesis, amino acids are linked by .... to form polypeptides. This process occurs at the ribosomes. The function of the ribosome is to hold the .... in such a way that its .... can be recognised and paired with the complementary .... on the *t*–RNA. The molecules manufactured by ribosomes situated on the .... of the cell may be converted to glycoproteins in the ....

Total 6 marks
[London]

Question 3

Coppicing is a technique of woodland management in which trees are cut down regularly. Open spaces or areas of reduced tree canopy are thus produced.

(a) The diagram below shows the food web in part of a coppiced woodland.

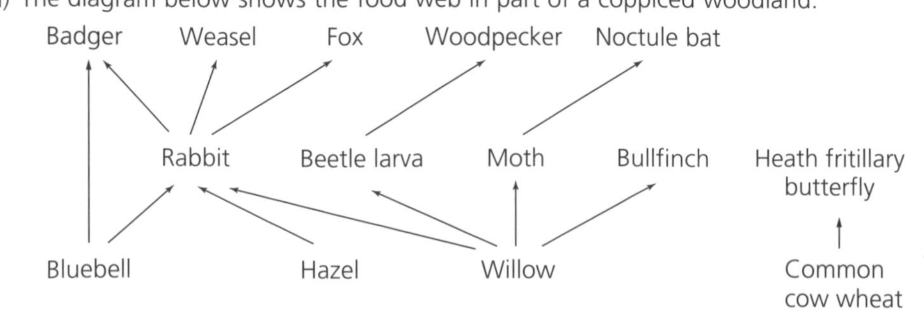

(i) State how many trophic levels are shown. [1 mark]
(ii) State why there are usually not more than *four* trophic levels in a food web. [1 mark]

(b) (i) Suggest how coppicing may change the ground flora of a woodland. [1 mark]
(ii) Suggest a reason why this change may occur. [1 mark]

Total 4 marks
[London]

Question 4

Maize cobs may have purple or red grains. This character is controlled by a single pair of alleles. The dominant allele *A* gives a purple colour and the recessive allele *a* gives a red colour.

(a) In an experiment, a heterozygous plant is crossed with a maize plant homozygous for allele *a*. State the genotypes of these two plants. [1 mark]

(b) Grain colour is also affected by a second pair of alleles. The presence of the dominant allele *E* allows the purple or red colour to develop, but in the homozygous recessive (*ee*) no colour will develop (despite the presence of alleles *A* or *a*) and the grain will be white. A plant of genotype *AAEE* is crossed with a plant of genotype *aaee*.
(i) State the genotype and phenotype of the offspring produced as a result of this cross. [2 marks]
(ii) The plants of the offspring are allowed to self-fertilise. Draw a genetic diagram to show the possible genotypes produced as a result of this cross. [3 marks]
(iii) Predict the phenotypic ratio that would be obtained from this cross. [3 marks]
(iv) Which genotypes, if allowed to self-fertilise, would produce pure-breeding lines containing white grains? [3 marks]

Total 12 marks
[London]

Question 5

Catalase is an enzyme which catalyses the breakdown of the toxic chemical hydrogen peroxide into water and oxygen. The enzyme is found in many tissues including those of potato tubers.

An investigation was carried out into the effect of pH on the rate of catalase activity in potato tuber tissue. The apparatus used in the investigation is shown below.

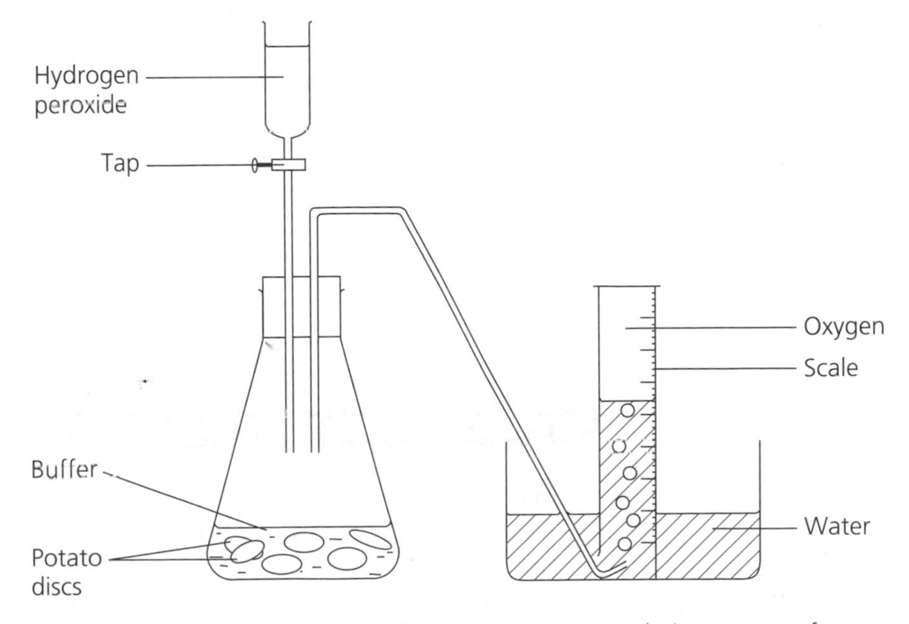

(a) (i) Suggest *three* suitable pH values for the experiment and give a reason for your choice. [2 marks]
(ii) State *two* conditions, other than pH, which should be kept constant during the experiment. [2 marks]

(b) (i) Describe how the apparatus would be used to measure the rate of catalase activity. [4 marks]
(ii) Suggest *three* sources of error which could occur during the experiment. [3 marks]
(c) Suggest why catalase is present in living tissue. [1 marks]

Total 12 marks

[London]

Question 6

The graph below shows the effect of temperature on the rate of photosynthesis in two grasses, *Agropyron* and *Bouteloua*.

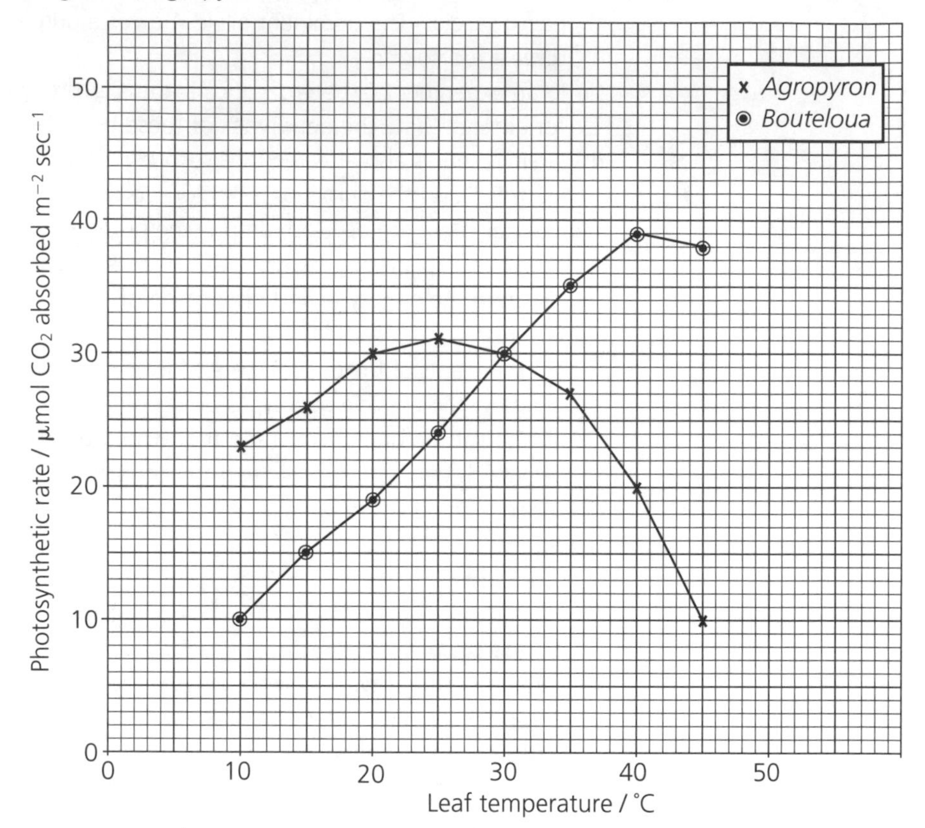

(a) From the graph, find the rate of photosynthesis at 22 °C for each of the grasses. [2 marks]
(b) Suggest which of the two grasses is likely to grow faster in a tropical climate. Give a reason for your answer. [2 marks]
(c) (i) Suggest why the rate of photosynthesis declines at high temperatures. [1 mark]
(ii) State *two* factors which can be limiting in photosynthesis. [2 marks]
(d) Describe a simple method that you could use in the laboratory to investigate the effect of temperature on the rate of photosynthesis in an aquatic plant. [4 marks]

Total 11 marks

[London]

TIMED PRACTICE PAPER 2

Free prose questions.

This style of question is set by many examination boards.

Each question should be completed in 30 minutes including planning time.

The mark for each question is 10 marks and you should think in terms of giving 10 separate relevant points to get full marks.

Answer any *two* questions, giving yourself one hour in total

Question 1
Give an account of the structure and functions of enzymes in living organisms.

Question 2
Write an essay on:
Support and locomotion in animals.

Question 3
Write an account of the dark reaction (light-independent reactions) in photosynthesis and explain how radioactive tracers have been used to study this pathway.

Question 4
Give an outline of the process of aerobic respiration and discuss the significance of this process in maintaining the composition of the atmosphere.

OUTLINE ANSWERS TO PAPER 1

Question 1
✓ ✓
✗ ✓
✓ ✗
✗ ✓
✓ ✓

Total 5 marks

Question 2
Each line gives alternative answers for a gap in the passage.
peptide bonds / condensation / polymerisation / enzymes;
messenger RNA / mRNA;
codons / triplets / bases / nucleotides;
anticodons;
endoplasmic reticulum / ER;
Golgi body / dictyosome / smooth ER

Total 6 marks

Question 3
(a) (i) 3 [1 mark]
(ii) The loss of energy at each trophic level limits the number. [1 mark]
(b) (i) Increase the number of species / introduce new species. [1 mark]
(ii) Increased light / increased insect population / change in water level.
Any of these points would gain the mark. [1 mark]
Total 4 marks

Question 4
(a) *Aa* *aa* [1 mark]
(b) (i) Genotype *AaEe*
Phenotype purple grains [2 marks]
(ii)

(gametes)	*AE*	*Ae*	*aE*	*ae*
AE	*AAEE*	*AAEe*	*AaEE*	*AaEe*
Ae	*AAEe*	*AAee*	*AaEe*	*Aaee*
aE	*AaEE*	*AaEe*	*aaEE*	*aaEe*
ae	*AaEe*	*Aaee*	*aaEe*	*aaee*

[3 marks]

The marks would be allocated as 1 for the correct gametes and 2 for the correct genotypes.

(iii) 9 purple; 4 white / colourless; 3 red [3 marks]
(iv) aaee; Aaee; AAee [3 marks]

Total 12 marks

Question 5

(a) (i) pH 3, 7, 9;
that is one acid, neutral and one alkaline [2 marks]
(ii) Any two of:
temperature; volume of buffer; volume / concentration of peroxide;
number / mass / surface area of potato discs. [2 marks]
(b) (i) Any four of the following would gain full marks:
Use freshly cut potato tissue;
equilibration of the solutions;
add peroxide and close tap;
collect oxygen for a stated time / time for production of a standard volume of oxygen;
read volume collected off the scale;
rate = volume divided by time;
replication with each buffer;
calculate mean rate of oxygen production at each pH. [4 marks]
(ii) Any three of the following:
Concentration of catalase in the discs may be variable;
hard to get the same surface areas of potato;
frothing may affect oxygen collection;
volume of gas depends on temperature;
apparatus may leak;
some oxygen will dissolve in the water [3 marks]
(c) Any one of these points:
removes toxic products / hydrogen peroxide is produced in metabolism. [1 mark]

Total 12 marks

Question 6

(a) *Agropyron* 30.5 μmol CO_2 absorbed m^{-2} sec^{-1}
Bouteloua 21 μmol CO_2 absorbed m^{-2} sec^{-1} [2 marks]
(b) *Bouteloua;*
higher rate of photosynthesis at tropical temperatures. [2 marks]
(c) (i) enzymes denatured [1 mark]
(ii) light intensity;
carbon dioxide [2 marks]
(d) Any four of these points would gain the marks.
Measure rate of oxygen production from the plant;
in container of water at stated temperature;
reference to constant light intensity;
repeat at a range of temperatures;
monitor temperature and keep it constant;
replication at each temperature. [4 marks]

Total 11 marks

OUTLINE ANSWER TO PAPER 2

Question 1

The question asks for structure and function of enzymes and so comments about both should be included in the answer. This answer includes five points about each aspect and would gain the full 10 marks.

Enzymes are made up of chains of amino acids forming polypeptides. The polypeptides are folded to give a globular structure, part of which forms the specific active site of the enzyme. The substrate of the reaction fits into the active site where the reaction takes place and the products separate from the enzyme.
Enzymes speed up the rate of a reaction. They lower the activation energy needed for the reaction to take place and so enable it to proceed faster and at a lower temperature. This means that the reactions can take place within living cells within suitable temperature limits. Enzymes are not changed in the reaction and so they can be used many times. Each enzyme functions most efficiently at a specific temperature, the optimum temperature. Similarly, they have an optimum pH at which they function most efficiently.

Other points which could have been included instead of some of the above are comments about:
specificity; prosthetic groups; induced fit; denaturation by high temperatures; reversibility; role in anabolism; role in catabolism; control of metabolic pathways.

Question 2
Support and locomotion in animals

This answer would need to be in essay form, i.e. have an introduction and a conclusion, so it would be best to plan the answer before beginning to write it, so that you avoid repetition and remember to cover all the relevant areas. In this type of answer, you will usually be awarded marks for the scientific content and the facts, and also for the way in which you have covered the topic. In addition, there is usually credit for the style, so you need to take some care with the way in which you express your ideas and ensure that you avoid grammatical and spelling errors.

Topics which it would be relevant to cover are as follows.
Some general introduction as to the need for support and the general functions of skeletons in providing this support. At this point it might be relevant to discuss the differences between the needs of animals living on land and those living in water.
Hydrostatic skeletons – a description – their role in movement – a suitable example – some comment on the advantages and disadvantages of such skeletons.
Exoskeletons – a description – reference to the need for joints – a suitable example – some comment on the limitations imposed on growth – ecdysis – advantages and disadvantages – some reference to the mode of locomotion of insects – walking – flying – could also be relevant in this section.
Endoskeletons – a description – different types of joints – different tissues involved in these skeletons – ligaments – tendons – a suitable example – advantages and disadvantages – some relevant comment on different types of locomotion such as swimming, walking, flying.
Some detail should be included of the anatomy and histology of striated muscle – the details of muscle contraction – synergistic and antagonistic action of muscle sets.
The exact details of your answer would depend on how much detail your syllabus contains on this topic.

Question 3

Make sure you spend time on both parts of this question in order to score a good mark. Diagrams can be used in both parts but it is unlikely that maximum marks can be gained using diagrams only.

In the first part, credit would be given for reference to the pathway of the carbon dioxide from the atmosphere to the chloroplast stroma, where it is fixed. Carbon dioxide is then picked up by the ribulose bisphosphate, under the influence of the carboxylase enzyme, RuBP carboxylase. A 6-carbon compound is formed which is unstable and which breaks down immediately into two molecules of 3-carbon phosphoglyceric acid (PGA). The PGA is phosphorylated and then reduced to give phosphoglyceraldehyde (PGAL), using ATP and NADPH from the light reactions. Most of the PGAL is used to regenerate the carbon dioxide acceptor molecule, RuBP. This involves a complex series of reactions. PGAL can be converted to hexose sugars and then to starch by condensation. Other organic compounds, amino acids and fatty acids are also produced.

Calvin used radioactive tracers in his experiments with the green alga *Chlorella*, trying to trace the sequence of products formed in photosynthesis. He used the radioactive isotope of carbon, ^{14}C. This was incorporated into hydrogencarbonate and supplied to the algae in a specially designed 'lollipop' apparatus. The algae were illuminated and allowed to photosynthesise for specified times and then samples were removed and analysed. The compounds containing the radioactive carbon were identified. By allowing the experiments to proceed for different periods of time, it was possible to trace the sequence of products.

Credit would be given for any correct details of the procedure and for any other experiments.

Question 4

This is any essay question and the first part of the answer requires some of the information presented in Chapter 3 together with some detail of what happens in the Krebs' cycle and the electron carrier system.

Reference should be made to the composition of the atmosphere and to the gas exchange which does go on between green plants and aerobic organisms to maintain the present equilibrium, before comments on how the balance can be upset by the activities of humans are made. It is relevant here to comment on the reduction of forests and plankton, and on the extra carbon dioxide being released by the burning of fossil fuels, but students must beware of losing their sense of proportion and haranguing the examiners about the evils of the greenhouse effect!